T0255975

Textile Science and Clothing Technology

Series editor

Subramanian Senthilkannan Muthu, Kowloon, Hong Kong

More information about this series at http://www.springer.com/series/13111

Subramanian Senthilkannan Muthu
Editor

Fast Fashion, Fashion Brands and Sustainable Consumption

 Springer

Editor
Subramanian Senthilkannan Muthu
Head of Sustainability
SgT group and API
Kowloon, Hong Kong

ISSN 2197-9863   ISSN 2197-9871   (electronic)
Textile Science and Clothing Technology
ISBN 978-981-13-4598-2   ISBN 978-981-13-1268-7   (eBook)
https://doi.org/10.1007/978-981-13-1268-7

This Springer imprint is published by the registered company Springer Nature Singapore Pte Ltd.
part of Springer Nature
The registered company address is: 152 Beach Road, #21-01/04 Gateway East, Singapore 189721,
Singapore

This book is dedicated to:
The lotus feet of my beloved
Lord Pazhaniandavar
My beloved late Father
My beloved Mother
My beloved Wife Karpagam and
Daughters—Anu and Karthika
My beloved Brother
Last but not least
To everyone working in the fashion
sector to make it SUSTAINABLE

Contents

Fast Fashion, Fashion Brands & Sustainable Consumption

Aline Buzzo and Maria José Abreu

Abstract The phenomenon of fast fashion chains is due to the way this business model manages its production chain and supplies. Combining the quick response to the agile, lean retailing and leagile processes, it is possible to deliver products to retail outlets in a few weeks, in response to growing consumer demand for new goods. The excessive consumption of fast fashion is also due to social media involves issues such as sustainability in fashion consumption and work practices within companies and their suppliers. On the other hand, the awareness of the concern with the consequences of this consumption gives rise to new ways of consuming and producing fashion causing less impact both environmental and social.

Keywords Fast fashion · Sustainability · Slow fashion · Social media
Value chain · Consumption

1 Introduction

The first chapter aims to reveal how the fast fashion business model works and how the processes involved in the production chain deliver new products to stores in a few weeks. The fast fashion concept first emerges in the late 1990s as a way of characterizing the rapid change in fashion and its form of consumption that some companies have begun to adhere to. According to Shimamura and Sanches (2012), "the phenomenon of fast-fashion, even though it is not a novelty in the sector, draws attention to the high profitability achieved and the continuous expansion" since when the model was adopted by major brands in the years 1990. Zara, a Spanish brand belonging to the Inditex group, is today the main representative of this marketing model. Still according to Shimamura and Sanches (2012) speed is an important part

A. Buzzo · M. J. Abreu (✉)
2C2T-Textile Engineering Department, University of Minho, Guimarães, Portugal
e-mail: josi@det.uminho.pt

A. Buzzo
e-mail: aline.buzzo@gmail.com

© Springer Nature Singapore Pte Ltd. 2019   1
S. S. Muthu (ed.), *Fast Fashion, Fashion Brands and Sustainable Consumption*,
Textile Science and Clothing Technology,
https://doi.org/10.1007/978-981-13-1268-7_1

of the process, but it is not the only characteristic. In addition to production speed, time, risk and cost must be taken into account in an efficient way. Ciettá (2010) argues that the ability of this system to manage risk-related problems effectively is one of the reasons for its success. The second chapter shows how the arrival of social networks accelerated the consumption of clothing and made them obsolete after being shown on the Internet, as well as the consequences on the consumption behavior of people, since, as Barnes and Lea-Greenwood (2006) explicitly explains, the chains of fast fashion had a negative impact on the environment, since many clothes in these business models are made of plastic fibers. It is important to note the change of habit use of the garments since the arrival of "fast fashion" chains as well as social networks. In a survey of 1500 women aged over 16 years, 33% of respondents said they considered the cloth old after wearing them just over three times, and one in ten women wear a garment only three times before it leave it at the bottom of the wardrobe (Barnardos 2015). It is necessary to take into account other materials used in the fashion industry, such as the metals of the trims, dyes and the entire process that involves the production cycle of a garment until it reaches the consumer, including ethical and labor practices, as it is reported in chapter three. Sustainability in the textile chain does not end when a garment arrives in stores. It still goes through labor practices and fair trade. India, for example, has the largest workforce in the fashion industry. About 35% of workers earn a salary equivalent to 80% minimum wage (Kerr and Landry 2017). A revolution in the way fashion is consumed is required, since each citizen is not only the audience but also produces, finances, collaborates and disseminates fashion (Carvalhal 2016). The alternatives to the excessive consumption in fashion through the creation of platforms of resales, loans and repairs of clothes are treated in the chapter four and, in chapter 5, the objective is to report how the slow fashion can be an important tool for the consicente consumption in the fashion.

The "slow food" movement, which emerged in Italy in the 1980s as a reaction to the growth of the fast food lifestyle, inspired the concept of "slow fashion" (Clark 2008). According to Fletcher (2007), the factor "time" is not so important in production, since the planning is done in the long term and does not requires subcontracting and temporary workers. In 2007, Hermés handkerchiefs, regarded as timeless and made at reduced speed due to special production techniques, were associated with "slow fashion". Therefore, many people still assimilate low speed to high-cost products (Deeny 2007). To preserve the natural resources that are consumed globally by the fashion industry, the "slow fashion" movement seeks to promote sustainable innovations, multifunctional and timeless design, reuse of textile materials and services based on alternative strategies such as leasing (or leasing) of fashionable garments and accessories (Angel and Gardetti 2017). Considering both forms of garment consumption, it is easy to deduce that the sustainability in fashion needs to be reflected throughout the textile production chain. Cotton and polyester are high on the list of textile materials most used in the fabric industry, and the polyester demand has doubled in the last 15 years (Fletcher 2013).

2 The Mechanics of Fast Fashion

The fast fashion companies seem able to do everything in less time compared to traditional companies, the point where we can ask ourselves how the latter can withstand the cyclone are going against them. Enrico Ciettá - *La rivoluzione del fast fashion*

The history of fast fashion back in the mid-1980s when the American mass production system across the ocean as highlights Doeringer and Crean (2006). According to Linden (2016), the dependence of large retailers on supply chains in developing countries has been directed by customer choice and increased exposure to ever-lower vineyard products. Linden (2016) points out that the process of industrialization and the beginning of wage labor stimulated the garment industry, as people no longer had time after work. To meet the demand of the sales season, it was necessary for retailers to make a large order, which generated large inventories that required equally large storage space. Thus, often the consumer demand was not understood and the retailer was forced to end of season sales (Doeringer and Crean 2006). To Ciettá (2010), retail ready-to-wear is as similar to the fast fashion, the speed of production and its availability as soon as the goods are ready. Previously, consumers had to pay a relatively high price to get access to the latest fashion trends. Today, fast fashion companies have made this access via their efficient production chain (Linden 2016). Therefore, speed is an important feature, but it is not essential to the operation of the fast fashion system. Cachon and Swinney (2011) point out that rapidly executed production increases the efficiency of product development, making the product range ready for sale at the start of the sales season, such as the North American brand GAP. The authors also point out that if retailers do not cut down on production time, even if they struggle within the design department, they run the risk of having to deliver the products too soon and thus miss last-minute trends (Cachon and Swinney 2011). Flexibility is, therefore, one of the fundamental elements to ensure a rapid replacement of merchandise (Bruce and Daly 2006). The biggest fast-fashion companies take their products to the stores in a few weeks. Zara, from the Spanish group Inditex, delivers its collections in two weeks; Forever 21 six weeks, and the Swedish H & M in eight weeks (Cline 2012). Linden (2016) points out that what makes fast-fashion products cheap comes from the immediacy of consumer demand, forcing the supply chain to deliver orders in record time. In addition, collections are not planned as in traditional fashion retail models. Instead, the search is only for the effectiveness of sales and the connection of company communication (Ciettá 2010). On the other hand, short deadlines allow companies to always keep up with trends (Cachon and Swinney 2011). The big fast-fashion retailers tend to diversify the product mix through sub-brands, each with its specific target and, therefore, caution is required in the differentiation of supply and communication within the company (Ciettá 2010). Rapid fashion companies do not hide that their products last about ten washes due to the poor quality of the raw material (Joy et al. 2015). What makes fast-fashion so successful? For Caro and Martinez-de-Albéniz (2015), the fast fashion business model can be explained by the combination of three elements: rapid response, frequent change of variety and fashion design at affordable prices, with the first two elements being of an operational nature and allows the operation of fast-fashion and, lastly, represents how the back-end operational create the business value proposition. What also differentiates the fast fashion model from the traditional fashion retail model is the absence of personality association from a single designer to the consumer, which makes him part of a global culture. It is no coincidence, therefore, that the largest fast fashion companies (H & M and Zara) are from countries that have no tradition of ready-to-wear clothing (Gabrielli et al. 2013). Cohen (2011) defines the fast-fashion model as a simple system that involves design, production, distribution, and fast marketing. However, not only the management of the production chain is responsible for the operation of fast fashion. Internal production is based on commercial studies and analyzes, using sales indicators and best-selling products (Ciettá 2010). According to Gereffi and Appelbaum (1994), the complexity of the fast fashion production chain is divided into five segments: commodities, component supply, production networks, sales channels and marketing networks. In view of the need to quickly deliver products at points of sale, the concept of Quick Response arises, based on the reduction of excess inventory in the supply chain, from the raw material to the consumer, in addition to reduce the risk of high orders, seeking to buy close to consumer purchases. "The use of the term Quick Response (QR) has evolved into a broader interpretation, which is conceptually very simple: postpone all risky production decisions, for example committing to purchases that may not be necessary in case of low sales, until there is enough evidence that market demand exists" (Caro and Martinez-de-Albéniz 2015). It can be further defined, according to McMichael et al. (2000), that the QR is a business strategy, aimed at the consumer, planned from the cooperation between the partners of the supply chain. In addition to the QR, the fast-fashion supply chain relies on other processes of equal importance, such as lean retailing, agile and "leagile" (Linden 2016). The lean retailing system aims to reduce the amount of inventory and thus minimize losses. The agile system has the ability to respond to demand in real time, and companies need to react to likely changes in demand using information technology (Christopher et al. 2016). The lean retailing system focuses on reducing loss and waste from within the company during manufacturing (Ohno 1988) in addition to the use of logistics innovation, team production and reorganized work environments (Taplin 2014). The "leagile" combines the processes of lean retailing and agile supply chains. Ciettá (2010) points out, however, that the industrial system of fashion goes beyond its importance in the manufacturing system. Rapid fashion companies are currently efficient both in terms of production, distribution, and are aware of consumer trends (Ciettá 2010). The consumption behavior, including, should be among the priorities of the fast fashion system. Linden (2016) cites the discovery of Professor Karen Miller, a professor of economics and marketing, in which most consumers shop for pleasure, that is, they are hedonic consumers. Yet for Barnes and Miller (2013), fashion companies use the hedonistic pleasures of consumers to make sales grow. Gabrielli et al. (2013) believe that the diversity of merchandise provided by large retailers increases the customer's desire to explore the store environment and acquire new products, and for some people this means discovering new styles and for others, means increasing and varying the amount of parts in the wardrobe. However, both the first and the second group do not expect the products to be of high quality, since they either will not use the parts as often or because they no longer expect purchases to be permanent. Added to this is the fact that, currently, access to the latest trends at affordable prices, through profitability through supply chains (Linden 2016). Linden (2016) further states that both demographic and socioeconomic transformations have led to changes in consumer behavior, as well as the disposition of cotton at low prices.

3   The Influence of Social Media on Non-sustainable Consumption

Social media are fundamentally changing the way we communicate, collaborate, consume, and create. They represent one of the most transformative impacts of information technology on business, both within and outside firm boundaries. Social media have revolutionized the ways organizations relate to the marketplace and society, creating a new world of possibilities and challenges for all aspects of the enterprise, from marketing and operations to finance and human resource management. Sinan et al. (2013) – *Social Media and Business Transformation: A Framework for Research*

Social networks have drastically changed the way we consume, above all, fashion. At first, social media was created for non-commercial use, but brands saw the opportunity to connect with their consumers through them (Wolny and Mueller 2013). Kamineni (2005) suggests that products and brands have the ability to convey messages to others from the products they use and thus styles dictate how consumers communicate. Consumers have become true co-creators and play a key role within fashion companies. Social networks act as a thermometer and, through them, it is possible to determine if a trend has been successfully adopted by a specific number of people or not, in addition to making possible the perception of the value of the product to the user (Wolny and Mueller 2013). Sinan et al. (2013) postulate that both companies and industries use social networks to promote and communicate with their target audience. For Elram and Orna (2015), consumers no longer depend on companies for information about a particular product. Even such companies use information provided by their own customers, turning them into researchers. Felsted and Kuchler (2015) point out that many young women, especially those born between 1982 and 2000, have become their own celebrity in the virtual environment, recording every moment of life and watching others. In peer-to-peer communication, users can choose what kind of information they want to share (Wolny and Mueller 2013). This spread is due to social networks, the greater the number of information found in them, the greater the chances of the consumer making the purchase choice that best meets their needs. Sanford Bernstein analyst Jamie Merriman believes that the "selfies" phenomenon makes young people shop more often, but because they do not have much income, they end up consuming retailers like Primark or Forever 21 (Felsted and Kuchler 2015). It is therefore essential to relate social networks to unsustainable consumption in fashion. Zara, the brand of Spanish group Inditex, has 24.9 million followers on Instagram, followed by Sweden's H & M (24.7 million) and Forever 21 (14.5 million) (Instagram 2018). According to a survey conducted by Barnardo's (2015) with 1500 women over the age of sixteen, 33% of respondents said they considered clothes old, if used more than three times, while one in ten women wear a garment only three times before leaving it in the back of the wardrobe. According to the survey, one in seven said social networks Facebook, Twitter and Instagram were strong influences on culture, because being "marked" in the same dress, even on different occasions, was unacceptable in fashion. Because of this, before the emergence of social networks, many people spent more on particular pieces of clothing because they were not as exposed as these days. That is why people have been consuming low-cost products to stay fashionable and thus to share their fashion pieces more often (Tan 2017). Although the fashion market has been late in reaching social networks, taking maximum advantage of them only after 2008 (Elram and Orna 2015), the fast fashion retailers have managed to keep up with the change in consumer behavior from information technology. During London's fashion week 2015, Topshop used Twitter to identify emerging trends and then immediately make their products available in their stores (Felsted and Kuchler 2015). This shows how companies need to understand this behavior change and gain benefits through social media (Heinonen 2011). Debra Aho-Williamson, an analyst at eMarketer, stresses that retailers should make e-commerce available on social networks, as it is where people spend most of their time (Felsted and Kuchler 2015). A report released by PricewaterhouseCoopers (2016) states that companies that are prepared to detect and manage consumers that influence others, strengthening their position among them and measuring their engagement will have a major advantage over their competitors. The social channels of companies are also fundamental in spreading brand sustainable actions, as H & M did, which involved influencers to share in their blogs the Conscious Exclusive collection, made entirely of sustainable raw material (Kang and Kim 2017). Social networks are therefore making the individual public, which forces people to engage with social media in one way or another, even if it is a professional social network, such as Linkedin (Sinan et al. 2013). Tan (2017) points out that in the world of social networks like Pinterest, Instagram and Snapchat, where people post what they are wearing very often, psychology in the way they use the same piece has changed and consumers want to feel belonging to the crowd and publicize your purchases. This new way of consuming fashion has caught the attention of fast fashion retailers, who have seen them take advantage of the shorter life cycles of these trends because they make consumers constantly looking for some product to satisfy themselves (Tan 2017). Such consumers appreciate the fact that what is in the stores today may not be in the next few days or weeks and thus fast fashion retailers can achieve a profit margin almost twice the average when compared to their traditional competitors, such as the department stores (Cline 2012). For Linden (2016), technology gives consumers access to a wealth of information about new trends and styles, playing a key role in customer loyalty. In addition, participating in social networking activities contributes to the sense of belonging of members of a social circle (Heinonen 2011). Within this context, nature undoubtedly suffers the consequences of the high consumption of fashion. Trying to follow the new trend, consumers incessantly consume clothing made of synthetic and polymeric textile materials (Barnes and Lea-Greenwood 2006).

4 Fast Fashion versus Fair Trade and Labor Practices

Consumers and micro-organizations alike identify sustainable fashion as being locally produced, which links to aspects of good working conditions, fair wages, and a reduced carbon footprint. Although these micro-organizations heavily feature the local aspect within their promotion, as it is seen as a vital selling point for sustainable garments, those consumers who doubt the quality standards of local production, do not necessarily perceive this as beneficial. Henninger et al. (2016) – *What is sustainable fashion?*

Sustainability in fashion permeates productive characteristics such as the use of eco sustainable and renewable materials, durability and longevity, and social attributes, including job security, fair wages and professional quality of life (Pookulangara and Shephard 2013). These factors have been widely discussed, especially after the Bangladesh accident in 2013, when the Rana Plaza building, a complex housing garment factories and supplies that supplied materials for large fast fashion chains, such as Primark, caused the death of more than 1100 workers (Butler 2016). This type of labor supported by exploitative practices may have emerged decades ago (or even centuries) when developing countries began to manufacture textiles extensively (Taplin 2014). In the 1980s, Mexico began to be replaced by China as one of the largest suppliers of textiles to the United States of America, after both had signed several bilateral agreements in order to make viable the capitalization of cheap labor (Taplin 2014). The fact of having a reserve of rural labor force of more than half a billion people makes China a possible first power in the world (Ciettá 2010). Intermediate companies, which are looking for cheap labor factories for outsourcers, have significantly increased the competitive pressures among these subcontractors, as they need to devalue their services to get more contracts since fast fashion emerged (Taplin 2014). This reflects intensely on the working conditions of this cheap labor. In Cambodia, for example, companies subcontract the demands of large retailers, even though they, to account for the number of orders, prohibit them. Labor causes activists criticize this subcontracting because it makes it difficult to trace the origin of the goods, preventing those responsible from being found (O'keefe and Narin 2013). The final price of the products of the main chains of fast fashion consists of only 1% of the manufacturing costs, according to Adams (2002). To reach this value, workers are forced to perform their duties in precarious conditions, often working for hours without rest in poorly ventilated environments (Adams 2002). In Honduras, 13-year-old girls were forced to work 13-h shifts at a factory under armed surveillance to make clothing from the Kathie Lee Gifford collection, later sold at Wal-Mart. Each worker received $ 0.31 per hour (Adams 2002). Child labor in the textile sector is even more delicate because it is "only a symptom of bigger problems," as Josephine Molds explains, for The Guardian Labs with UNICEF data. Within the textile chain some functions are more suitable for children, such as picking cotton for example. Its small fingers prevent or reduce losses during harvesting (UNICEF). It is estimated that 170 million children are somehow part of the labor force in the textile chain in the world, which is equivalent to 11% of the world's children (UNICEF). In Cambodia, the minimum age for work is 15 years, but the lack of labor inspection makes it possible to hire girls up to 12 years old, who drop out of school to help their families through underemployment (Quinn 2017). Most of the factory workforce are women, who have their working condition even more aggravated if they become pregnant. The pregnant worker often have their wages reduced and may even be dismissed. Moms who stay on the job work through the night to meet the deadlines, to gain extra hours for it, which forces them to spend a lot of time without going home (Quinn 2017). According to a report issued by the National Labor Committee of Bangladesh, of the 1.6 million textile workers in the country, 85% were young women between the ages of 16 and 25, working between 12 and 14 h a day for 7 days in the week (NCL 2001). To meet consumers' demand for a wider variety of products in the shortest possible time, in order to always be part of the current trend, fast fashion companies resort to low-cost hiring, which causes competition between subcontracted factories, reflecting directly on excessive work and very low wages (Taplin 2014). The fast fashion industry, in the impetus of having their demands met, eventually led subcontractors to search for increasingly cheap labor. Workers who are obliged to comply with these working conditions free of charge (UNICEF). One of the tools used to promote underground factory reforms is "codes of conduct," which are guidelines with restrictions or prohibitions on the use of forced labor, fair wages, and collective bargaining rights (Adams 2002). The Fair Labor Association (FLA) was created from the union of companies in the clothing, consumer and labor sector to claim the vigilance of 30% of the 4000 factories of its members by 2005, increasing the number of factories by 10% per year monitored (Adams 2002). An article on the website Portugal Têxtil (2018) points out that, after releasing the annual sustainability report for 2017, the Swedish fast fashion brand H & M reveals the progress made in several areas such as circular economy, sustainability and labor practices. However, the results have been rebutted by workers' rights group Clean Clothes, which alleges non-compliance with the agreement, signed in 2013 by the brand on improving its labor practices. The group notes that the report does not provide data on the salaries paid to its suppliers. The Millennial generation, born after 1980, makes up the conscious part of consumers, who react to ethical practices and cherish those companies that are concerned with offering products that are in line with their values (Kronfeld et al. 2017). The fight must also start with all consumers in general and producers. But governments play a key role: oversight. Slave labor is illegal in all countries, and although the population puts pressure on those responsible and businesses in general, the government must legally secure labor rights when they are disfellowshipped (Kronfeld et al. 2017).

5 Buy and Borrow, Leasing and the Collaborative Consumption

The sustainability of fashion is not only determined by the material, the design, and produc-tion conditions, but also by consumers and their intentions, behaviors, and habits. Samira Iran e Ulf Schrader - Collaborative fashion consumption and its environmental effects

It is well known that exacerbated consumption is responsible for major problems in the ecosystem. One of the outputs for this problem is the reduction of new pur-chases, reuse of products already acquired (Piscicelli et al. 2015). The collaborative consumption (CC) has been pointed out as a promising business in the sense of reducing the impact caused by the rampant consumption, especially of fashion prod-ucts. It is already possible to notice a great number of initiatives supported in the principle of sharing, although it is not yet dominant (Pedersen and Netter 2015). The concept of collaborative consumption is defined by Hamari et al. (2016) as a peer-to-peer (or "peer-to-peer") activity, where obtaining, sharing or accessing ser-vice goods through online or offline platforms can also generate economic benefits. In a historical context, the collaborative consumption of fashion has already been inserted into local communities, neighborhoods and families, and its most obvious result is to extend the life of garments before being discarded. Traditional retailers have felt the impact of collaborative fashion consumption (CFC) through revenue losses. For a number of years, the goal of academic and professional research was to understand how production and legislation within the fashion industry could reduce environmental impacts, in the production phase, it was tried to change the practices, focusing on the raw material used and the technology applied to the production and the salaries paid to those involved in the process, as described in Fig. 1 (Iran and Schrader 2017).

Iran and Schrader (2017) classify collaborative fashion consumption into two categories: P2P (peer-to-peer) and B2C (business-to-consumer). In the P2P model fashion products are passed from consumer to consumer and the interaction can be carried out through online platforms. The second model (B2C) is characterized by the interaction between company and consumer, in which the company mediates the rent or purchase of products. In this case, consumers are less engaged because the company provides the mechanisms required for transactions. Generally, participation in these communities is free, and is compensated for by participations in the form of advertising. In order to understand what motivates individuals to make purchases based on virtual collaborative consumption, Johnson et al. (2016) interviewed 30 people. Among the motivations identified, the most cited were functional, social, environmental, personal and economic, the latter being a main motivation, since the participants wanted to save more money by making collaborative purchases. Comfort and ease consisted of the functional factors while the reciprocity of support among the other users formed the social motivation. Ecosystem motives, on the other hand, included a desire to reduce unnecessary waste and thus protect the environment. The personal factors were formed by the desire to follow the fashion and have fun with this new form of consumption. WRAP, a UK-based company specializing in sustain-

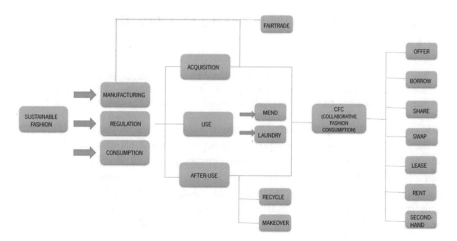

Fig. 1 Collaborative fashion consumption (CFC) as an element of sustainable fashion (Adapted from Iran and Schrader 2017)

ability actions, conducted extensive research on valuing clothing within consumer behavior with 7950 British adults over the age of 16 (WRAP 2012). It was found among the participants that 30% of their clothes had never been used for at least a year, usually because they no longer fit. The research also found five areas that offer feasibility for the economy of resources and money, both by companies and by consumers, according to Fig. 2.

Within these spheres, the institute highlighted opportunities for businesses and consumers to secure these savings. Among these opportunities, they emphasize the

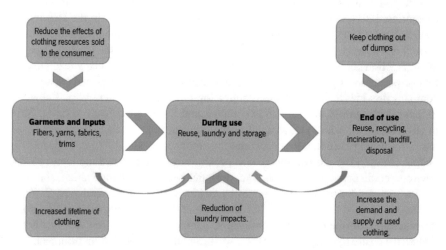

Fig. 2 The core opportunities to save money and resources across the clothing life cycle (Adapted from WRAP 2012)

concentration in a positioning by the companies so that they offer products of greater quality in order to increase their durability. At the same time, the consumer for searching for new ways to use the same piece and thus ensure longer life to it. This lengthening of clothing usage time could save £5 billion per year in the cost of laundry, laundry and disposal. Several factors make the consumer use a part for a longer time, among them the desire to continue using it (either combining it in different ways or buying parts already used, for the classic and versatile design) and the individual's ability to repair or modify their clothing (WRAP 2012). Some of WRAP's (2012) approaches to saving money and resources during the clothing life-cycle include reducing the consequences of clothing processes to customers without packing products into landfills, increasing the shelf life of clothing, reducing impacts washing and increasing the supply and demand for secondhand clothes. The report points out that although the consumer has a strong interest in extending the shelf life of his clothes, he has difficulty clearly understanding the communication by companies about the quality of their products. However, for retailers, there is still no consensus that if the product's validity is increased, its cost will automatically be raised as well. Still, both consumers and companies know that low-cost products have their lifetimes reduced after frequent uses and washes (WRAP 2012). Within the scope of sustainable consumption of fashion emerges a business model that focuses on expanding the time of wearing a clothing while people save money on parts that would be used only a few times. Fashion libraries offer rental opportunities (where each piece has a value to be borrowed) or leasing (a kind of compulsory signature that is converted into clothing rentals) rather than the sale and works on virtual platforms or physical. It is, therefore, an alternative to the traditional consumption of fashion, where one has access to new clothes without having to accumulate large volumes in the cabinets. It is fundamental that fashion libraries have a good relationship with customers, both in physical space and in virtual space, because members value the social value of the experience of changing clothes and are happy to participate in the history of each one of them (Pedersen and Netter 2015). An example of a fashion library is the Nu Wardrobe, which began as a periodic exchange virtual store, enabling its customers to consume fashion in an accessible and sustainable fashion. One of the advantages of the platform is its sustainable operation, since it eliminates all the costs of a physical store. A low fee is charged to keep the cost of running as low as possible (O'Reilly 2018). As already mentioned, the Z and Millenial generations have been searching for more ethical ways of consuming fashion, while keeping up with trends in the market. At the same time, the incentive to re-use ends up attracting people who care about consuming products that minimize the environment (Chiquoine 2017). In an article for the WGSN, Jackie Chiquoine (2017) refers to these generations of consumers as being great boosters of sustainable consumption through digital platforms resale of fashion products. Social media are therefore key players in enabling this peer-to-peer sales trade, which also targets customers with few resources (Chiquoine 2017). Open source software, file sharing, online membership, and peer-to-peer financing are different spheres of collaborative economics, which has spawned technology developments that have simplified the sharing of products and services (Hamari et al. 2016). Jackie Chiquoine also quotes data from a survey conducted by Fung Global Retail Tech, where the growth of reseller start-ups is expected to expand five times faster than conventional retail. In a survey of intentions to buy in collaborative consumption, it has been revealed that people tend to adhere to collaborative consumption when they know someone who has had this experience. This allows marketers to use people's experiences to engage other consumers (Lennon 2014), in an article for The Guardian, emphasizes the obsolescence of fashion, which leads to short breaks in clothing purchases (which we are wearing less and less) and most of the times it is not compatible with its cost per use. It is likely that fast fashion will not disappear, but fast use may be more sustainable in the future (Lennon 2014).

6 Slow Fashion and the Value Chain

> Slow fashion is about designing, producing, consuming and living better. Slow fashion is not time-based but quality-based (which has some time components). Slow is not the opposite of fast – there is no dualism – but a different approach in which designers, buyers, retailers and consumers are more aware of the impacts of products on workers, communities and ecosystems. Kate Fletcher – *Slow Fashion*

The concept of slow fashion derives from the movement of slow food, created in 1986 by the Italian Carlo Petrini, who excels in the appreciation of food and care throughout the food production chain. Slow fashion is based on the identification of sustainable fashion solutions as well as strategic repositioning of design, production, consumption and reuse, allowing the individual to be fashionable in a more ethical way (Clark 2008). Slow fashion especially represents a different way of consuming clothes, leaving from being in quantity to being with quality. When slow fashion companies begin to drive their production to smaller, more quality-oriented fashion cycles, it seeks to make it easier for consumers to purchase superior quality products that they can use for longer (Magnuson et al. 2017). Within ethical clothing, characteristics of environmental responsibility, welfare of employees and animals, and slow fashion are ways of influencing consumption of ethical fashion (Magnuson et al. 2017). In contrast to slow fashion, fast fashion does not allow equilibrium in the value chain—from production to disposal by the consumer—and is disconnected from the current context, either due to low wages, overtime, and climate change caused by the process of textile production (Fletcher 2007). Remy et al. (2016), in an article for McKinsey, raises important current data on fashion production and consumption. From 2000 to 2014 the number of garments doubled, reaching 100 billion, which would give about 14 garments per person on the planet. Five of the largest developing countries (Brazil, China, India, Mexico and Russia) together had their apparel sales eight times faster than in Germany, Canada, the United States and the United Kingdom. It is also estimated that if 80% of the emerging population were to consume equally what consumes the western world, and if the fashion industries were not aligned with sustainability, the environmental trail left by the sector would be extremely large. In order for this problem to be eliminated, companies need to measure the performance of their sustainable development throughout the production and supply chain, defining improvement goals (Remy et al. 2016). In addition to manufacturers targeting their customers to good consumer practices and helping to maintain their clothing longer, companies may also be able to combine information technology to enable customers to track the production process of each product, as the company has developed EVRYTHING software and the manufacturer of Avery Dennison packages (Remy et al. 2016). Slow fashion is inextricably linked to the textile and fashion value chain, bringing to the fore the responsibility for cleaner production, treatment of tributaries, use of biodegradable or sustainable materials, independence of the internationalization of the production process, more tax burdens fair conditions and decent work conditions (Rúbia 2014). However, large-scale production, the classical techniques of production and the use of local raw materials become obstacles given the speed of fashion and the standardization of styles (Ferronato and Franzato 2015). Fashion is a way to connect people globally, assuming that clothing is now idealized, manufactured and marketed in different parts of the world. Social media plays an important role in sharing ecologically sound production initiatives (Kang and Kim 2017). The slogan "think globally, act locally" characterizes the locale as a manifesto and focuses on bringing people a sense of global commitment (Clark 2008). Slow fashion enables suppliers to plan production and organize the workforce that will be responsible for it, so they do not need to hire temporary workers or force them to work overtime to meet the demand. It is common, then, that the increase of the quality of a product or service reflects directly in the final price of the product. But we will be dealing with goods of greater value, extended durability and that are part of a fair and sustainable production chain in all scopes, as Fletcher (2007) ponders. Fletcher (2007) argues that "slow design allows for richer interaction between designer and creator; manufacturer and clothing; clothing and user". The slow manufacturing process contributes to a fairer labor environment, improving workers' quality of life and ensuring mandatory labor rights, without excessive factory loads or extraordinary demands (Jung and Jin 2014). In a survey by Watson and Yan (2013) it was found that fast fashion customers increase the life of the parts by buying as much as possible and at the lowest price, spending as little as possible on each piece. Slow fashion consumers, meanwhile, extend the life of their parts by investing in versatile, well-molded products that fit the existing pieces in their wardrobes. This behavior prevents slow fashion customers from regretting their purchases with ease, as they focus on quality rather than quantity (Watson and Yan 2013). Distinctions between consumerism for pleasure in fast fashion and slow fashion customers explain the reasons for each one of them. While the fast fashion consumer takes pleasure in "bulk" purchases from large retailers, slow fashion consumers guarantee their hedonism by making conscious and sustainable purchases (Watson and Yan 2013). Slow customs help to create a delayed dialogue on the rules and goals of fashion that meet the principles and economic needs (Fletcher 2010). Slow culture still provides the popularization of fashion (though not at such low prices), but allows people to have control over corporations and technologies that directly interfere with their lives (Fletcher 2010).

7 Conclusion

The proposal from the chapter was to analyze consumer behavior within fashion using fast fashion and all its mechanics (from its emergence, operation and logistics to the way it persuades the consumer) as a starting point. Short production time, a complex and efficient logistical process, the use of international financial agreements and a franchising system were some of the success elements of Benetton, a large Italian fast fashion chain (Ciettá 2010). Fast fashion prioritizes the design of a collection that is mostly composed of best sellers but delimits a specific style and is consistent with each other. This purpose requires large retailers to always be aware of the latest stylist releases (Ciettá 2010). Different academic sources that approach fast fashion classify their supply chains in different modalities, such as just in time, lean retailing, quick response and "leagile" (Linden 2016), and the just in time process aims to increase the selection of goods in reduced cycles of products with lower demands, which decreases store inventory and quickly produces what is being consumed by customers (Doeringer and Crean 2006). Fast fashion systems target small pre-season purchase orders coupled with speed and versatility over the seasons, and by sharing information across all sectors of the supply chain, it is possible to know clearly, what consumers are buying (Barnes and Lea-Greenwood 2006). It is well known that social media and information technology are of fundamental importance to both generate the sense of urgency of fashion consumption and the dissemination of new ethical and sustainable practices for the acquisition of clothing and clothing accessories. The great networks of fast fashion should not reject the power of social media since they are the main tools of exchange of information about products and services (Rodríguez and Fernandez 2017). Within the consumption of fast fashion, important data were collected from the fashion industry, as well as from its textile production chain and how it affects the planet in the social and environmental spheres. Exaggerated alternative practices are becoming increasingly common, especially considering the spread of access to social media and how they enable the exchange of experiences and business models, underpinning what is called a circular economy. Sharing and leasing products means discarding less and using more, which is healthy for the ecosystem and for our self-image (Walsh 2011). The emergence of these new ways of consuming fashion is due in particular to the slow fashion movement, which translates into consumer behavior the concern of people to consume fashion in an ethical and sustainable way, without giving up being within the latest trends. Therefore, slow fashion has its own characteristics, such as awareness of the consequences of fashion on ecosystems and society, and ends up involving consumers in the production process (Hall 2017). This chapter also revealed important data on labor practices in the fast fashion production chain, including forced labor (child and adult), lack of time off, wages far below what was stipulated by law, and prohibition of the formation of collective agreements. In extreme situations factory workers are kept in captivity, with the most basic civil rights being taken away. The lack of regulation by countries that house subcontracted factories further aggravates the situation of these workers, who cannot count on any organ or union to intercede for their rights (Adams 2002).

References

Adams, R. J. (2002, May). Retail profitability and sweatshops: a global dilemma. *Journal of Retailing and Consumer Services, 9*(3), 147–153.

Angel Gardetti, M., & Torres, A. L. (2017). *Sustainability in fashion and textiles: Values, design, production and consumption.* New York: Routledge.

Barnardos. (2015). [Online] Available at: http://www.barnardos.org.uk/news/press_releases.htm?r ef=105244. Accessed 26 Janeiro 2018.

Barnes, L., & Lea-Greenwood, G. (2006). Fast fashioning the supply chain: Shaping the research agenda. *Journal of Fashion Marketing and Management: An International Journal, 10*(3), 259–271.

Barnes, L., & Miller, K. (2013). Hedonic customer responses to fast fashion and replicas. *Journal of Fashion Marketing and Management: An International Journal 17*(2):160–174.

Bruce, M., & Daly, L. (2006). Buyer behaviour for fast fashion. *Journal of Fashion Marketing and Management: An International Journal, 10*(3), 329–344.

Butler, S. (2016). *The Guardian.* [Online] Available at: https://www.theguardian.com/world/201 6/jan/28/bangladesh-factory-safety-scheme-stalls, acessado em 21/03/2018. Accessed 30 March 2018.

Cachon, G. P., & Swinney, R. (2011). The value of fast fashion: Quick response, enhanced design, and strategic consumer behavior. *Management Science, 57*(4), 778–795, 4 Mar 2011.

Caro, F., & Martínez-de-Albéniz, V. (2015). Fast fashion: Business model overview and research opportunities. In: N. Agrawal & S. Smith (Eds.), *Retail supply chain management* (pp. 273–264). Boston: Springer.

Carvalhal, A. (2016). *Moda com propósito - manifesto pela grande virada* (1st Ed.), São Paulo: Paralela.

Chiquoine, J. (2017). *WGSN.* [Online] Available at: https://www.wgsn.com/content/board_viewe r/#/74660/page/1. Accessed 30 March 2018.

Christopher, M., Van Hoek, R., & Harrison, A. (2016). Creating the agile supply chain: Issues and challenges. In: K. S. Pawar, H. Rogers, A. Potter & M. Naim (Eds.), *Developments in logistics and supply chain management* (pp. 61–68). London: Palgrave Macmillan.

Ciettá, E. (2010). *A revolução do fast fashion - estratégias e modelos organizativos para competir nas indústrias híbridas* (1st Ed.), São Paulo: Estação das Letras e Cores.

Clark, H. (2008). SLOW + FASHION—an Oxymoron—Or a promise for the future …? *Fashion Theory, 12,* 427–446.

Cline, E. L. (2012). *Overdressed: The shockingly high cost of cheap fashion* (1st ed.). S.L.: Penguin.

Cohen, A. M. (2011). Fast fashion: Tale of two markets. *The Futurist, 45*(5), Sep-Oct 2011.

Deeny, G. (2007). Fast forward to slow fashion. *Financial Times.*

Doeringer, P., & Crean, S. (2006). Can fast fashion save the US apparel industry? *Socio-Economic Review 4,* 353–377, 1 Sep 2006.

Elram, M., & Orna, S. L. (2015, December). Fashion conscious consumers, fast fashion and the impact of social media on purchase intention. *Academic Journal of Interdisciplinary Studies,* 173.

Felsted, A., & Kuchler, H. (2015). *Financial Times.* [Online] Available at: https://www.ft.com/con tent/bef817ae-31f1-11e5-91ac-a5e17d9b4cff. Accessed 28 March 2018.

Ferronato, P. B., & Franzato, C. (2015). Open design and slow fashion for the fashion system sustainability. *Modapalavra,* October, Issue Special, pp. 104–115.

Fletcher, K. (2007). *The Ecologist.* [Online] Available at: https://theecologist.org/2007/jun/01/slo w-fashion. Accessed 30 March 2018.

Fletcher, K. (2010). Slow fashion: An invitation for systems change. *Fashion Practice,* Novembro, pp. 259–266.

Fletcher, K. (2013). *Sustainable fashion and textiles: Design journeys* (1st Ed.), Londres: Earthscan.

Gabrielli, V., Baghi, I., & Codeluppi, V. (2013). Consumption practices of fast fashion products: A consumer-based approach. *Journal of Fashion Marketing and Management: An International Journal, 17*(2), 206–224.

Gereffi, G., & Appelbaum, R. (1994). Power and profits in the apparel commodity chain. In: E. Bonacich, et al. (Eds.), *Global production: The apparel industry in the Pacific Rim* (pp. 42–62). Philadelphia: Temple University Press.

Hall, J. (2017, April 27). Fast fashion, slow fashion? *Fashion Theory—The Jorunal of Dress, Body and Coulture, 25*(1).

Hamari, J., Sjöklint, M., & Ukkonen, A. (2016, September). The sharing economy: Why people participate in collaborative consumption. *Journal of Association for Information Science and Technology, 67*, 2047–2059.

Heinonen, K. (2011, December 23). Consumer activity in social media: Managerial approaches to consumers' social media behavior. *Journal of Consumer Behaviour*, 356–364.

Henninger, C. E., Alevizou, P. J., & Oates, C. J. (2016). What is sustainable fashion? *Journal of Fashion Marketing and Management: An International Journal, 20*(4), 400–416.

Iran, S., & Schrader, U. (2017). Collaborative fashion consumption and its environmental effects. *Journal of Fashion Marketing and Management: An International Journal, 21*(4), 468–482.

Johnson, K. K. P., Mun, J. M., & Chae, Y. (2016). Antecedents to internet use to collaboratively consume apparel. *Journal of Fashion Marketing and Management: An International Journal, 20*(4), 370–382.

Joy, A., Sherry, J. F., Venkatesh, A., Wang, J., & Chan, R. (2015). Fast fashion, sustainability, and the ethical appeal of luxury brands. *Fashion Theory 16*(3), 273–295.

Jung, S., & Jin, B. (2014, July 15). A theoretical investigation of slow fashion: sustainable future of the apparel industry. *International Journal of Consumer Studies, 38*, 510–519.

Kamineni, R. (2005, October). Influence of materialism, gender and nationality on consumer brand perceptions. *Journal of Targeting, Measurement and Analysis for Marketing, 14*(1), 25–32.

Kang, J.-Y. M., & Kim, J. (2017, March 30). Online customer relationship marketing tactics through social media and perceived customer retention orientation of the green retailer. *Journal of Fashion Marketing and Management: An International Journal, 21*(3), 298–316.

Kerr, J., & Landry, J. (2017). *Pulse of the fashion industry*. Copenhagen: Global Fashion Agenda & The Boston Consulting Group.

Kronfeld, M. J., Brown, A., & Herb, J. O. (2017). *Millenial Magazine*. [Online] Available at: https://millennialmagazine.com/2017/07/27/fast-fashion-how-slavery-fuels-your-style/. Accessed 30 March 2018.

Lennon, N. (2014). *The Guardian*. [Online] Available at: https://www.theguardian.com/sustainable-business/sustainable-fashion-blog/2014/oct/02/how-to-be-fashionable-without-owning-clothes, acessado em 29/03/2018. Accessed 29 March 2018.

Linden, A. R. (2016). An analysis of the fast fashion industry. *Senior Projects Fall 2016*.

Magnuson, B., Reimers, V., & Chao, F. (2017). Re-visiting an old topic with a new approach: The case of ethical clothing. *Journal of Fashion Marketing and Management: An International Journal, 21*(3), 400–418.

McMichael, H., Mackay, D., & Altmann, G. (2000). Quick response in the Australian TCF industry: A case study of supplier response. *International Journal Of Physical Distribution & Logistics Management, 30*(7/8), 611–626.

Moulds, J. (n.d.). *The Guardian Labs*. [Online] Available at: https://labs.theguardian.com/unicef-child-labour/. Accessed 30 March 2018.

NCL. (2001). *National Labor Committee*. [Online] Available at: www.nlcnet.org. Accessed 20 February 2018.

Ohno, T. (1988). *Toyota production system: Beyond large-scale production*. Portland: Productivity Press.

O'Keefe, K., & Narin, S. (2013). *The Wall Street Journal*. [Online] Available at: https://www.wsj.com/articles/SB10001424127887324787004578497091806922254. Accessed 30 March 2018.

O'Reilly, R. (2018). *Fashion Revolution*. [Online] Available at: https://www.fashionrevolution.org/ireland-blog/a-case-for-borrow-not-buy/. Accessed 29 March 2018.

Pedersen, E. R. G., & Netter, S. (2015). Collaborative consumption: Business model opportunities and barriers for fashion libraries. *Journal of Fashion Marketing and Management, 19*(3), 258–273.

Piscicelli, L., Cooper, T., & Fisher, T. (2015, June). The role of values in collaborative consumption: Insights from a product-service system for lending and borrowing in the UK. *Journal of Cleaner Production, 97*, 21–29.

Pookulangara, S., & Shephard, A. (2013). Slow fashion movement: Understanding consumer perceptions—An exploratory study. *Journal of Retailing and Consumer Services, 20*(2), 200–206.

PricewaterhouseCoopers. (2016). *PWC.* [Online] Available at: https://www.pwc.es/es/publicac iones/retail-y-consumo/assets/moda-por-un-tubo-relacion-cliente-omnicanal-sector-moda.pdf. Accessed 27 March 2018.

Quinn, S. (2017). *Listverse.* [Online] Available at: http://listverse.com/2017/03/17/10-truly-troubli ng-facts-about-the-clothing-industry/. Accessed 30 March 2018.

Remy, N., Speelman, E., & Swartz, S. (2016). *Mckinsey.* [Online] Available at: https://www.mckin sey.com/business-functions/sustainability-and-resource-productivity/our-insights/style-thats-su stainable-a-new-fast-fashion-formula. Accessed 30 March 2018.

Rodríguez, T. E., & Fernandez, R. B. (2017). Facebook practices for business communication among fashion retailers. *Journal of Fashion Marketing and Management: An International Journal, 21*(1), 33–50.

Rúbia, D. (2014). *Audaces.* [Online] Available at: https://www.audaces.com/slow-fashion-produca o-consciente-na-moda/. Accessed 30 March 2018.

Shimamura, E., & Sanches, M. C. d. F. (2012). O Fast Fashion e a identidade de marca. *Projética Revista Científica de Design*, Dezembro, pp. 66–76.

Sinan, A., Dellarocas, C., & Godes, D. (2013, January 14). Introduction to the special issue—Social media and business transformation: A framework for research. *Information Systems Research*, 3–13.

Tan, O. (2017). *Adweek.* [Online] Available at: http://www.adweek.com/digital/oliver-tan-visenze-guest-pot-fast-fashion/. Accessed 24 March 2017.

Taplin, I. M. (2014). Who is to blame?: A re-examination of fast fashion after the 2013 factory disaster in Bangladesh. *Critical Perspectives on International Business, 10*(1/2), 77–83.

Têxtil, P. (2018). *Portugal Têxtil.* [Online] Available at: http://www.portugaltextil.com/hm-e-o-sal ario-injusto/. Accessed 19 April 2018.

Walsh, B. (2011). http://content.time.com/time/specials/packages/article/0,28804,2059521_20597 17_2059710,00.html. [Online] Available at: http://content.time.com/time/specials/packages/arti cle/0,28804,2059521_2059717_2059710,00.html. Accessed 18 March 2018.

Watson, M. Z., & Yan, R.-N. (2013). An exploratory study of the decision processes of fast versus slow fashion consumers. *Journal of Fashion Marketing and Management: An International Journal, 17*(2), 141–159.

Wolny, J., & Mueller, C. (2013, May 20). Analysis of fashion consumers' motives to engage in electronic word-of-mouth communication through social media platforms. *Journal of Marketing Management*, 562–583.

WRAP. (2012). *WRAP.* [Online] Available at: www.wrap.org.uk/sites/files/wrap/VoC%20FINAL% 20online%202012%2007%2011.pdf. Accessed 29 March 2018.

Fast Fashion and Sustainable Consumption

Faustine Binet, Ivan Coste-Manière, Clément Decombes, Yan Grasselli, Dortmolk Ouedermi and Mukta Ramchandani

Abstract Summer dresses in January and winter coats in July, fast fashion have never been so fast! A world globalization trend to ever changing the fashion industry, it made global brands to adopt a seasonless cycle of designing clothes and relocating manufacturing activities at underdeveloped countries in a way to support the cost of mass production, but the transition went with ignoring the working conditions and the environmental costs. Fast fashion led to several disasters that have had a huge impact on planet earth and the overall humanity, it also led to a massive consumption along with unsustainable demand, this is not the extraordinary consumption of ordinary people but rather the ordinary and fast consumption of ordinary people if we want to divert the quote of Bernard Dubois, professor at HEC, in "The Art of Marketing". Fast fashion is today subject to unsustainable progress that is frustrating an entire economy with a big shift in consumers' behavior, and this fact raised the debate around the problem of sustainability in the apparel industry. So, it is interesting to see how sustainability may generate a new perspective to the fashion industry, by bringing not only the most innovative strategies and technologies into the production process, but also the most genuine ideas to satisfy the need of fashionable customers,

---

In Memoriam to our friends, students and much more, our beloved Cédric Laguerre and Keryan Grimault.

F. Binet · I. Coste-Manière (✉) · C. Decombes · D. Ouedermi
SKEMA Business School, Suzhou, China
e-mail: ivan.costemaniere@skema.edu

I. Coste-Manière · Y. Grasselli
SKEMA Business School, Sophia Antipolis, France

I. Coste-Manière
SKEMA Business School, Belo Horizonte, Brazil

I. Coste-Manière
Sil 'Innov & Eytelia, Courcelles, Belgium

M. Ramchandani
United International Business School, Zurich, Switzerland

M. Ramchandani
Neoma Business School, Reims, France

© Springer Nature Singapore Pte Ltd. 2019   19
S. S. Muthu (ed.), *Fast Fashion, Fashion Brands and Sustainable Consumption*,
Textile Science and Clothing Technology,
https://doi.org/10.1007/978-981-13-1268-7_2

that are not interested anymore in only acquiring the latest trends, but also involved in promoting a more sustainable fashion to a point of spreading a new mindset for pushing consumption toward consciousness, and especially to forge an ethical appeal for brands, it goes to say that the problems behind sustainability brought a radical change to the fashion industry and it may play to its advantage for having different concepts and resourceful solutions. So, can fast fashion be sustainable?

Keywords Sustainable · Fast fashion · Consumption · Customer centric · Triple bottom line · Fast luxury · Hard luxury · Human scale development

1   Context and Method

The 21th century, seems to be the century of you are what you buy, and you buy to be. Even mainstream movie such as *Confession of a shopaholic* seems to emphasize this need of buying. Buying could be a new part of the Maslow pyramid. This frenzy around buying is using more and more resources and create poor working conditions for the worker in the garment industry. Fast fashion is the top emerged part of the iceberg that impacted earth resources and society. However, in the same time, public and corporation are aware that the resources are limited, this paradoxal thoughts set foot in western society. They want to buy but at the same time they know that buying too much could damage the planet and could not be sustainable on a long term vision. So for fast fashion corporation they have to make a choice between staying the way they are and in 20 or 30 years not being able to reach public demand or find a way to be sustainable.

In this article we will first explain what sustainable means, because people tend to think that sustainable development is just an environmental protection thinking, and how its link to fashion. We will try to show that Fast fashion is born from a long term strategy from fashion industry but also from the consumers itself. Then we will try to show how fast fashion try to be sustainable and what they are doing to be this way.

2   Sustainability, a Blurry Concept

2.1   An Historical Overview

Sustainability, is a big word, born in the late 80's from the Brundtland report (1987), which put the basis of what could be thereafter becoming "sustainable development". This report came after oil crisis, that rose public and corporation awareness about the fact that resources are not unlimited; the eighties are also marked by several environmental and industrial catastrophes. Those catastrophes had a huge impact on the public opinion and this idea of protecting environment and resources started to grow in people's mind. Therefore, United Nations decided to play a role in the protection of resources and environment, and create an Environment and development commission. The aim of this commission was to determine how corporation and countries could improve and protected their resources and environment. In this report entitled *Our common future*, the commission set the outline and gives the definition of sustainable development as a kind of *development that satisfies the needs of the present without adversely affecting the ability of future generation to satisfy their needs.* At the beginning of the nineties, an economist Manfred Max-Neef tried to refine the definition gave by the Brundtland Report, by explaining in opposition with the Maslow theory, that human have fundamental basics needs. This theory of development is described has «*Targeted and based on the satisfaction of basic human needs, on the creation of more high level of autosuffisance, and on the construction of organic articulation between, Human, nature and technology, between global process and local activity, between individual level and social level, between planification and autonomy and between civil society and State.*» Max-Neef et al.; *Human Scale Development; an Option for the Future* (1991). This concept of enter twined dimensions, that depends on the other finds an echoes at the Earth Summit in Rio Janeiro in 1992, the summit popularized this concept of three dimensions connected to each other's, that will become later, sustainable development. The three dimensions are Environment, Society and Economy. The connections of those dimensions were expressed by three main ideas. The first one was that economic, social and ecological processes are connected and that the action of both public and stakeholders can't be considered had isolated, this first idea highlight the interrelationship between the three dimensions. The second idea was about the intergenerational aspects, sustainable development means more than just the present environmental protection; it is also the understanding that our present needs and the processes implemented to fulfill them will have an impact on the next generation. The third idea is about economy. Sustainable development in order to be efficient and real needs a long-term structural shift in how economy and society are managed. Meaning that government and institutions needs to find a way to reduce environmental impact and resources consumption while maintaining an efficient economy and social cohesion.

2.2   How Do We Define Sustainability

The definition of sustainability in people's minds is really different from the vision corporation or institutions have, it link to how sustainable is marketed. Buzzback and Rainforest alliance have made a global study in 2014, to try to define what Sustainability means. They have interrogated 2000 people from US, UK, China, Brazil and India. The top of mind association when it comes to sustainability for consumer is green, natural, recycling, two-third of the people interrogated feel that way. But when it comes to social responsibility, responsibility and moral, consumers don't feel like it meet with their personal values. Moreover, we see that sustainability could be an argument for marketers, indeed 80% of the people interrogated said that they are more willingly to buy a product with a sustainability label on the package, this concern about sustainable is strong among the new generation such as Generation X and the Millennials. But for brand it's a challenge to incorporate such message into their brand messaging, and until now, it have more easier for them to communicate on the green aspect, and it the reason why so many people think that sustainable is link to environment. But marketers should start now to explain that sustainability can have real benefits for an healthier environment, improved living conditions … Therefore this study shows the importance of communication from the company to raise public awareness, but at the same time it raise the issue of greenwashing because companies could be tempted to communicate on fake sustainability efforts while in reality nothing is really done. As the public does not see transparency, ethics and moral as most important issue when it comes to sustainable, there is no need to prove or give proof of their efforts. Consequently, how public see sustainability is link to how corporation promote it; and even if they are willing to support it, they are reluctant to check how company enforce a sustainable strategy.

We can say that "sustainability" is a word that companies use as promotional tools, and that even if the concern is real and institutions try to enforce change in the way industries and companies works, they need the help of the public to force those changes. In this era of over-surconsumption is sustainable a reality especially for fast fashion.

3 Fast Fashion, a Trend that Become a Strategy

3.1 The Birth of Fast Fashion

> This is not the extraordinary consumption of ordinary people but rather the ordinary and fast consumption of ordinary people

if we want to use the quote of Bernard Dubois, professor at HEC, in "The Art of Marketing".

Fast Fashion is a new trend which appears during the 80's–90's in United Kingdom. Big brands discovered this niche market where they can produce quicker and cheaper compare to their home countries such as Europe where the labor cost has increased within this period of time.

This sector is similar to the well-known Fast-Food industry. The aim of both activities is quickly producing and quickly distributing products which are constantly renewed. This concept has now been adopted as a business model by brands and retailers, using improved and more efficient supply chains to better respond to changing trends and consumer demand.

Fashion decided to go abroad in poor or developing countries such as India or China which are now, the main countries for clothes manufacturing. These two countries have flexibility and the ability to adapt their productions really quickly. This is one of the first reasons for the emergence of Fast Fashion.

Short time and large production capacity with extraordinary adaptability has enabled China and India to become world leaders in this sector. This is where the evolution of Fast-Fashion begins as we went from two historic seasons a year: Spring/Summer and Autumn/Winter, to more than 52 "micro-collections". Which is about one collection per week. The goal here is to push consumption to its apogee.

Collections have been created at first to increase the sells as each collection has a unique footprint which makes them more or less "old-fashion", dated, outdated and thus create this feeling of frustration in the mind of the consumer so that they buy more to fill that feeling and have the satisfaction of being "fashionable".

When we talk about fast-fashion, we are not talking only about the production capacity, or even the creative capacity of the different fashion brands, since that would not exist if there were no customers for renewing stocks and thus the different collections.

In order for this to work efficiently, it is necessary to have prices that match with the demand of the market. As these collections are quickly outdated, the price has to be inexpensive, first to manufacture and secondly to sell/retail. It is much more difficult to make haute couture in fast fashion since the design of these clothes requires a certain know-how and expertise, especially time, because many details are handmade. There is no doubt mass production is needed at a low labor force cost.

When it comes to purchasing, we would like to understand how this fast-fashion industry is now one of the powerful in the world. Customer behaviors is a part of the answer.

3.2   From "Cogito Ergo Sum" to "Buy so You Could Be"

We all have said: "Every day I have to dress up; I buy and bought a lot of clothes. I know have a huge closet and I never have anything to wear. I can never put together a coherent outfit."

This sentence shows us how people are affected and addicted to fashion. We communicate who we are through clothing. It has been like this for years and years with these historical examples we will try to understand how fashion and customer behavior has changed to lead to fast-fashion consumption.

During the 17th century, Louis XIV, the Sun King decreed it was mandatory to change outfits at least 3 times a day.

Louis XIV, one of the most powerful kings ever in France, decided to move all products upmarket to impoverish every aristocratic families, so they cannot set up a rebellion.

In a certain extent, no one can derogate from the king's rules even in term of Fashion. This is where in the History we discovered the importance of clothing and self-image. The pressure of the social environment was heavy. People wanted to attract the sympathy of the King by following all these rules in order to get better positions, more money… In the same time Louis XIV realized that, and created himself "total look", from head to toe outfit for the court. He chose the most expensive raw materials and colors and created at the same time his sumptuary laws in 1708 who codified and framed the garment. One cannot derogate, neither in terms of colors, nor in terms of forms…, in order to avoid commoners dress like the nobility. All the court went into debt and at this point, we saw the birth of a new phenomenon in France, which was fashion and the French haute couture.

Later on, with the emergence of the constitutional system, premise of democracy, and the emergence of the bourgeoisie in France, the fashion industry turned upside down.

We saw two segments of customers appear. The first was the historical affluent consumers who could afford to buy "tailor-made" goods and the second one, the bourgeoisie who tried to gain esteem by buying fashion and luxury goods.

This particular social class will rise to power during the period of great stability of the Second Empire. They are not like aristocrats; they have no ranks, no blood, and no land to insure their backs. They only have their fortunes of the moment. They must show it and convince others of their powers.

An event, however, will be the premise of what will become an unprecedented social movement, the emancipation of women.

However, in 1852, a man named Aristide Bouciccaut decides to create a new kind of trade. We are in the midst of the industrial revolution and in the midst of an overhaul of Paris, thanks to the work of Baron von Haussmann.

By creating the Bon Marché, this entrepreneur took the risk of targeting a female-only clientele of all social classes. He creates a department store with a profusion of merchandise from around the world, and where quality is guaranteed.

It is a new paradise of abundance and beauty as Emile Zola describes it in his work Au Bonheur des Dames.

Prices are now indicated on each article and the capacity of judgment is thus relayed to the women, and no longer to the merchant who was allowed to estimate the capacity of purchase of these customers according to its only judgment.

The fundamental feature of this society is change and movement, be it space, masses, individuals, goods, ideas … Traffic and nomad is the key word. Emile Zola, one of the great observers understood that circulation and speed were the foundations of modernity.

> I want in the "Au Bonheur des Dames", to make the poem of the modern activity (…) In a word, to go with the century, to express the century, which is a century of action and conquest, of efforts in all the senses.

With a place dedicated to them, women discover that they have a body, needs and desires, which until then was only reserved for men.

Moreover, in 1851, an innovative machine was created to facilitate the way of producing goods; its name is the SINGER sewing machine. The fashion industry has been totally reshaped; it allowed fashion companies to produce clothes in bigger quantities. It is also the time of size standardization. Clothes were for all of them tailor-made, however you cannot produce in a large quantity if you have to adapt each clothes to each morphology. This is one of the reason why size standardization has been the solution to make fashion industry more profitable in term of lower cost of production for cheaper prices. Cheaper prices also had a result on increasing the sales.

It as well had a huge impact on the consumption and on the consumer behavior for one main reason: Frustration.

The main motivation for buying clothes at that time was self-image and social class recognition, customers got frustrated when they could not buy a dress they liked because it didn't fit. Thus, people began to buy more and more to counter this feeling of frustration. Purchasing became a necessity to compete against the other bourgeois to really set up their rank in the society.

These historical facts really show what is the problem nowadays, it hasn't changed that much. Today people are buying more and more in order to stay fashion and satisfy a need. Consequently, people spend more and more money into clothing, thinking it's cheap so they can afford it, in fact they become poorer and poorer and make this fast fashion industry growing faster and faster.

In the old days, every fashion brands had catwalks and fashion shows to exhibit their creation to clients and yet this is completely different with today's fashion industry, we shift to a way of producing in order for companies to make big interests.

We just have to look at the following figures to state on this. During the 1960's almost 95% of the garment district clothing sales were made in the United States unlike today it only represents roughly 3%.

Subcontracting and outsourcing has been the best answer for companies increasing their profit. The idea here is, at less price they will produce it, at less price they will sell it but in bigger quantities.

A study conducted by l'Institut Français de la mode shows the importance of this trend nowadays.

In 2011, European Union countries imported 67.7 billion euros of clothing from around the world. An increase of 22% in five years and 8% over one year, despite a gloomy economic situation. The first export country is China with more than 18.9 billion euros clothing export in 2006. Importing clothes in the European Union is growing year on year.

The EU is Bangladesh's main trading partner, accounting for more than 24% of Bangladesh's total trade in 2017. In 2015, Bangladesh was already the EU's 35th largest trading partner in goods, imports from Bangladesh being dominated by clothing, accounting for something like 90% of the EU's total imports from Bangladesh. From 2008 to 2017, EU28 imports from Bangladesh have almost trebled to something like €16,000 million, which represents almost half of Bangladesh's total exports.

Import of clothing in billions of euros to the European Union

Country	2006	2007	2008	2009	2010	2011	Var. (%)
Bangladesh	4.6	4.4	4.7	5.2	5.9	7.5	63.04
Cambodia	0.6	0.5	0.6	0.5	0.6	0.9	50.00
China	18.9	21.9	25.3	25.7	28.5	29.7	57.14
India	3.8	3.8	3.9	4.1	4.2	4.6	21.05
Indonesia	1.4	1.2	1.1	1.1	1.1	1.2	−14.29
Morocco	2.4	2.5	2.4	2	2.1	2.1	−12.50
Pakistan	0.9	0.9	0.9	0.9	1	1.3	44.44
Sri Lanka	1	1	1.1	1.2	1.2	1.3	30.00
Thailand	0.9	0.8	0.8	0.7	0.8	0.7	−22.22
Tunisia	2.5	2.6	2.6	2.3	2.3	2.4	−4.00
Turkey	8.2	8.9	7.9	7	7.9	8.2	0.00
Vietnam	1	1.1	1.2	1.2	1.4	1.7	70.00

Source Institut Français de la mode

Habillement (Vêtements maille et chaîne et trame)		% de Variation 2016/2015	Textile		% de Variation 2016/2015
Chine	27 681 967	-8%	Chine	9 753 346	2%
Bangladesh	14 845 814	8%	Turquie	4 911 462	3%
Turquie	9 506 203	1%	Inde	2 650 750	2%
Inde	5 120 596	0%	Pakistan	2 404 248	5%
Cambodge	3 367 701	14%	Corée du Sud	1 096 892	-3%
Vietnam	2 993 648	7%	États-Unis	1 095 136	-12%
Maroc	2 528 706	9%	Suisse	812 239	-1%
Pakistan	2 454 428	8%	Japon	651 349	10%
Tunisie	1 957 033	-2%	Égypte	445 427	-7%
Sri Lanka	1 456 979	-8%	Taiwan	441 087	-5%
Indonésie	1 293 381	1%	Indonésie	402 393	-8%
Suisse	693 952	2%	Bangladesh	383 645	3%
Myanmar	676 178	61%	Vietnam	340 555	4%
Hong Kong	613 807	-9%	Thaïlande	316 845	0%
États-Unis	559 029	0%	Tunisie	271 756	0%
Thaïlande	463 762	-9%	Maroc	253 607	14%
Macédoine	452 317	-1%	Israël	231 106	2%
Égypte	391 384	-3%	Australie	220 950	22%
Serbie	374 753	7%	Nouvelle-Zélande	145 368	-1%
Madagascar	337 188	11%	Afrique du Sud	137 231	25%

INSTITUT FRANÇAIS DE LA MODE

Source GTA
Calculs IFM

EU apparel and textile imports in 2016—IFM

More than the amount of the exports itself, it is interesting to focus on countries evolution.

Bangladesh and Vietnam became more and more attractive for European companies in terms of manufacturing costs.

Since 2000, China has become France's leading clothing supplier. Its entry into the World Trade Organization and the gradual lifting of quotas had a positive impact on its trade.

China remain the main importer country for two reasons, first manufacturing costs are lower than in Europe even though minimum wages had increase in the last decades, secondly European Union voted in 2005 the dismantling of quotas on imports goods which caused an inflow of Chinese goods.

Nevertheless, the 2005 agreements also benefited countries such as Bangladesh and Vietnam. These two countries have specialized in clothes making during the past years. They have major advantages compare to China: wages cost, which are way lower and unions got no power and rights. Government and politics put pressure on the market to remain the most competitive on the international scene which leads to some disasters.

When we talk about pressure and subcontracting, companies understood their power on their suppliers, this is what we will call the law of free competition. This new fast fashion business model transformed the way clothes are produced. Companies want to get the best price regarding at what retail price their competitors are selling their clothes and so these companies will put pressure on their suppliers to get to the price they want. Almost all the time companies such as H&M or Forever 21 succeed. We have to understand suppliers need this contract, because there is a lot of competition and big companies make them dream of a long-term relationship which is for a small or medium size company a guarantee of not going into bankruptcy.

Subcontracting production have another strength, which is the non-responsibility on any issues, which can occurred in the factory. Legally they do not own the plant, every criticizable decisions taken by the factory management team do not concern or incriminate them in any ways.

For this reason, it can lead to catastrophic events such as the Rana Plaza collapse which killed almost 1200 persons. This factory was the main H&M supplier at this time. When we talked about the huge bargaining power they had on these factories to reach the lowest price of production it indirectly involves them on these disastrous situations.

These companies argue and justify themselves by offering jobs to people which had no chance to get one. They are helping these countries to develop their market and increase people buying power.

When Zara is offering $5 t-shirt retail price we all know that the working conditions can't be exemplary. Factories have to strain employees in order to fulfill their target.

Rana plaza was not the only consequences of that, in 2012 a fire destruct Ali Enterprises in Pakistan caused the death of 289 garment workers, during the same year in Bangladesh a fire lead to about 112 deaths and so on and so on.

It is rather paradoxical because the year after Rana plaza's collapse, fashion industry results were the most profitable of all time.

Fast-Fashion clients were regardless on those aspects; they were and still stay focusing on materialistic values. Their image, money and social statues are drivers which guide their life. They reach this feeling of happiness through shopping. They are also depressed and anxious, this is where advertising make an important role on the buying decision. They sell us the possession of goods as something that makes us happy.

If we look at the Maslow's hierarchy of needs, we will see how advertising is playing on every level to influence people on buying, from the basic needs to the least ones, and the self-fulfillment needs (achieving one's full potential including creative activities).

- Clothes are basically a physiological need, dressing is a need we can derogate from. We all have to wear clothes in order to go to work, to school, in the street… It is a basic need.
- We also all need a job, safety but it makes us feel stressed and anxious, as there is more qualified jobs in our western countries.
- Belongings and love needs, this stage is really important, we all need friends and a family but, in our society, to get into a group of friends most of the time they will judge us by our outward appearance. We need to be fashion or to express who we are by clothing.
- Esteem is almost the same as the previous stage. The fashion industry has huge impact on our society guided by rules and trends people have to follow to be recognized as a modern woman or man.
- Self-Actualization: "I buy so I am", this quote well summarizes the idea here. Showing what you can buy makes you more confident especially if it is accepted and values shared by all.

Fast-Fashion advertising plays in every stage of this hierarchy by selling a message of satisfaction after purchase.

We all have problems in our life we need to solve and their message is really waving on this trend.

Thus, advertising makes you feel old-fashion, fat, not in trend really quickly as they always advertise and as people are all the time exposed to these messages. Fast-fashion industry has this a huge advertising power, they advertise everywhere at any time.

The more they advertise on our conquest of happiness the more we feel comfortable and uncomfortable so the more you buy. This lead to an overconsumption of clothes that means more waste, more pollution and more sustainable issues.

As a result, people around the world collectively consume more than 80 billion items of clothing each year, and those items are increasingly seen as disposable.

Earnest Elmo Calkins a pioneer advertiser in the 20th century talked about this new phenomenon as Consumptionism. He described an ideology, system of beliefs, that prioritizes consumption and spending above all else.

Companies such as H&M also use celebrities image and luxury brands awareness to boost their sales by launching capsule collections.

The most representative partnership with H&M is Jimmy Choo. Customers became hysterical about having a pair of Jimmy Choo shoes, a jacket designed by the famous designer Karl Lagerfeld or even buying a dress from the Italian brand Versace.

The main objective, through these sales, is to sell the idea of making a great deal: We buy a pair of shoes Jimmy Choo by H&M, but it is not a real pair of Jimmy Choo, a Karl Lagerfeld jacket H&M is not a reflection of the Chanel house, or even of Karl Lagerfeld.

Overconsumption can be companies driven by advertising, novelties every week, low price, and their presence all around the world but overconsumption can be led by clients also.

Social medias play an important role on overconsumption lead by clients. The aim of social media such as Facebook, Twitter, Instagram and YouTube is to share your life to everyone. When it comes to shopping people are sharing their purchase online in order to expose what they like and what they can afford. Each person can have different motivation for doing that but belongingness is one of the main driver, they prove themselves they made the right choice but purchasing this instead of this. Social medias are also a way to interact with people; it means you can interact with someone who will give you his/her opinion on one product or another which will comfort you on your next purchase decision. This is the reason why we saw this new blogger phenomena come out in the recent years.

Word to mouth and the influence of your peer also has nowadays an impact on the consumption for the same reasons.

To conclude this part, Fast-Fashion is one of the most powerful industry nowadays leading by overconsumption of customers but during years, fast-fashion brands known as H&M, Forever 21, Zara, Primark, Topshop and so forth have played with production costs by relocating there production abroad with complete impunity by ignoring the working conditions of workers and disregarding the environmental impact provoked by this over-production.

This has led to several disasters that have had a huge impact on the image of these brands.

4   Fast Fashion: Can It Be Sustainable?

Sustainable fashion is today the most debated topic and an undergoing competition worldwide, it could be identified as an umbrella term to describe ethical, green, and eco fashion; Then, according to the Free Encyclopedia, it could be defined as the trend of sustainability and part of the growing design philosophy, developed to create a system which can be supported in terms of human impact on the environment and social responsibility. From a first insight, it could be considerate as an alternative trend against fast fashion, whereas new structures are designed to reduce or partially eliminate the detrimental impact of mass producing clothes, adding to that different mechanisms are set to work on relatively improving the apparel industry and promoting new ethical standards.

Sustainability is making a radical change in the fast fashion industry and a revolutionary move to reduce the society's obsession with relentless consumption. So, the highlights are mainly about the methods that will help to develop a sustainable fast fashion and how to ensure a possible future for this industry in a constantly challenging environment.

4.1   Triple Bottom Line Approach: The Definitive Quest

All over the world, a bottom line approach became an influential tool to address sustainability issues, it was at first discussed in 1999 by "the green business guru" John Elkington in his book "Cannibals with forks", the author demonstrated how this approach can help society achieve the three inter-linked goals of economic prosperity, environmental protection, and social equity at the same time to build a sustainable business. Then, it is very important to understand what kind of approach needs to be employed to build effective sustainable systems, because actors in fast fashion are responding differently to the sustainability movement, implementing different ways to counteract the problem, bringing green strategies to their business model and conceivable solutions to the production supply chain. In such a manner, to address sustainability concerns, giant retailers may need to operate and use a triple bottom line approach as a main measurement tool to be able to identify the effectiveness of their practices and to help them value the progress and efficiency of their systems.

Generally, this tool needs to cover three pillars: social vibrancy, environmental integrity, and economic prosperity, which goes to say that a perfect alignment between these may result in viable, livable, and equitable operations. This approach provides equal importance to both social and environmental impacts, encouraging enterprises to associate sustainable materials and actions with their growth strategy.

The concept of sustainable fashion was raised by the late of the 1980s, when Patagonia and Esprit were the first clothing companies to introduce and start the idea of manufacturing and marketing sustainable clothes, not to mention that they have been mastering a compelling slow fashion model, which successfully contributed to grow their activities through eliminating any noxious impact, and that's thanks to a great blend between economic, social, and environmental perspectives. What is more, these brands have always been leading the fight against fast fashion and according to a case study run by the firm Intelecom Intelligent Telecommunications: "Patagonia and Esprit have been pioneers in a growing category of companies that have successfully integrated social responsibility with profit. Both companies have prospered in the fiercely competitive garment industry, where consumers have become more demanding not only of product and service quality, but of corporate integrity as well."

For years, very few companies followed this kind of initiative, but since the urge for sustainability have been significantly debated in the fashion industry, large brands had no other way than to deal with this eventual change. This might be the case of H&M, which have been putting determined efforts to deal with this problem, and there is no doubt that they are being more transparent regarding their activities, they have stimulated a huge talk for their sustainability work, such as dedicating an online sustainability site open to a wide public and launching different recycling programs to encourage consumers to bring their used clothes to any H&M store, and then promising a new life-cycle to unwanted clothes.

But how come that a large brand of its kind been promoting sustainability more than ever?

A take-back strategy is what H&M is adopting, it actually consists on developing schemes that aim to tackle fashion's huge waste problem, as reported by Karl-Johan Persson, CEO of H&M "we are taking a circular approach to how fashion is made and used. That includes a more effective use of resources, support of innovations within recycling technologies as well as an increased use of existing or new sustainable materials."

The Ellen MacArthur Foundation believes that a conversion to a circular global economy in fast fashion is necessary, and they refer to the circular economy as an industrial economy that is restorative by intention; aims to rely on renewable energy; minimizes, tracks, and hopefully eliminates the use of toxic chemicals; and eradicates waste through careful design.

Unfortunately, this kind of approach could be effective at a small scale and it is only focusing on the environmental aspect, for example it doesn't support the working conditions in underdeveloped countries; Again, it will be interesting to see how the giant H&M is responding to social sustainability, they do only recognize that they have no direct control over the process of manufacturing clothes because they collaborate with independent suppliers. Then, due to the lack of appropriate methods, large corporations are not able to bring to bear such a move, because the nature of the fast fashion model creates limitations and obstacles when it comes to implement sustainability programs, especially that some global brands cannot easily modify their production and marketing process as long as the size of their company is steadily growing, this fact is also participating in giving them the possibility to manage only few aspects of their activities, and thus forcing them to contend with a situation in which few feasible solutions are available to figure out adjustments that may suit needs without harming both the profitability and image of the brand.

4.2   Issues in Sustainable Fashion

From an environmental perspective, it seems hard to slow down fast fashion, as reported by Mark Sumner that by 2030, it is predicted that the industry's water consumption will grow by 50% to 118 billion cubic meters, its carbon footprint will increase to 2791 tons and the amount of waste it creates will hit 148 tons…These facts motivated brands to enhance their work on reducing water pollution up to 50% and to have the possibility to implement chemical saving schemes, also the initiative of organic cotton use has reduced the quantities of textile waste ending in landfills.

But, a major point in the fashion industry is unsustainable demand. Today, the consumer behavior is problematic to develop sustainable systems, because it constitutes the major force driving fast fashion, it identifies how giant retail manufacturers are responding to a constantly growing demand for more clothing. An average consumer is always requesting the latest trends and outfits that has short-life cycle, and he or she is willing to spend more on affordable items, favoring an unstoppable process of rapidly producing high quantities of clothes at low costs, and even worse at underdeveloped countries where human labor is suffering from low wages and bad working conditions.

Then, since sustainable clothes are synonym to high quality product which is contradictory to the principles of fast fashion, the cost became the most challenging factor for implementing a green business model, for example in the case that a fast fashion brand decides to use organic garments it will affect its costs at all the levels along with increasing the prices, and consequently reducing the purchasing behavior of consumers that will engender great profit loss.

So, to which extent fast fashion could be opposite to sustainable fashion, and how is it possible that fast fashion brands are increasing awareness around this topic?

From a technical aspect, engaging in eco-friendly programs along with maintaining profits may accuse some brands of greenwashing activities and educating a new trend of consumerism to a whole generation. Then once more, as far as H&M is making efforts for ethical fashion we can't hide the truth that it's the most criticized brand for greenwashing, especially that the brand launched in 2013 "Recycle your clothes" program, which encourages consumers to bring back their used clothes at any H&M stores with an incentive of a 15% voucher to encourage more consumerism and then increasing the unsustainable demand. Also, in 2016 they heavily promoted the "world Recycle Week" for collecting 1000 tons of clothing, without taking into consideration the time for recycling clothes, it doesn't make any clear forecast for the efficiency of recycling the collected clothes, as the journalist Lucy Siegle reported on her opinion for the greenwashing activity behind this event, providing some calculations: H&M aimed to collect 1000 tones of clothes which could be the amount of clothes a retailer of this size can produce under only 48 h, whereas it will take 12 years for H&M to use the fashion waste! Adding to that, as published by Carolyn Beeler on December 2017 (reporter at the PRI, a global non-profit media company) on how good is the recycling program of H&M, it appears that the recycling process is not only recovering expanded steps, but the result is somehow deceiving, because when we think about the conscious line and recycled clothes, we tend to imagine that huge amounts of products are recycled, while only 7% of H&M's textiles is recycled, on account that 60% of collected clothes goes to re-wear and second hand and nothing more than 5–10% of clothes is recycled into fibers, without mentioning that the rest is downcycled into lower value products as stated by Catarina Midby sustainability manager at H&M UK and Ireland.

This means that fast fashion brands are dealing with sustainability without maximizing the risk of loss, they still need to offer affordable clothes to satisfy their consumers and to remain profitable.

Another major point is the inability to clean up the past, the social sustainability talks in fast fashion started after the occurrence of disastrous events, such as the collapse of the Rana Plaza in Bangladesh that killed 1138 people, researchers and activists claim that working conditions have hardly improved for garment workers due to a lack of control over independent factories suppliers, for example it was reported that workers are still producing clothes for H&M at plants that doesn't provide emergency exists. As a report on H&M factories overseas published by the Guardian in 2016, after conducting interviews with 251 workers at 12 H&M suppliers in Cambodia and four suppliers in India, it appears that workers are still having fixed duration contracts and they are suffering from an extensive work flow, it was reported by the Wage Alliance that the 12-h set by H&M on the weekly overtime limit is not respected by a nine to 17 h a day. This example illustrates how fast fashion brands are unable to control their manufacturing process because they depend on external parties.

4.3 Future of Sustainability in Fast Fashion

A promising future for sustainable fast fashion will be around great investment in innovations and new technologies. It is still hard for large manufacturer to create new means of producing natural garments; they need to come up with innovative recycling techniques to fasten the process from using recycled clothes. In this manner, the Swedish retailer H&M, in response to its insufficient recycling program, launched a reward competition for innovative ideas to handle the waste problem. Recently, an article was published by the fast company on March 2018 titled "5 innovations that could help make fast fashion more sustainable", it puts in advance the global award-winning innovations of 2018 that may have a significant impact on the future of fast fashion, all of these innovations are selected for the competition launched by the H&M Foundation:

- Smart Stitch: This innovation is one of the early-stage designs to enter the competition, it is an impressive technique to move from a linear model to a circular approach, thanks to the use of a new type of thread, if a shirt is heated to a certain temperature (266 degrees), the zippers and buttons fall off and the fabric can be used to create new clothes. But, this method requires intensive labor work to dissemble materials, so it clearly depends on companies and their willingness to invest in new technologies.
- Crop a porter: The concept consists of creating fabrics from crop waste, to deep into details; it is a new process of extracting cellulose from the waste of pineapples and bananas to create new fabric and textile, but also a way to reduce the greenhouse gas emission from the waste and a new source of income for the farmers.
- Algae Apparel: This method has a double function, it promotes compostable clothing through the process of harvesting algae that has no environmental impact as cotton, and it can also be used to dye clothes when breaking down a part of the algae into powder. Adding to this, the designers claim that it will also be beneficial to wear next to the skin thanks to its antioxidants characteristics.
- Fungi fashion: This design is hard to imagine, it grows mycelium in the shape of a garment and the thread is like the part of a fungus. Plus, there is no waste from using this method and it could be easily composted and buried in the ground.
- The Regenerator: Finally, this process consists of breaking down cotton-polyester thanks to the use of a mild chemical, which leaves the cotton intact to be successfully reused again.

These solutions can have a meaningful impact on solving the waste issue and encouraging innovative ideas may open doors of opportunities, consequently resulting in bringing a new sustainable cycle to the fast fashion industry. As reported by Erik Bang on the innovation lead of the foundation: "We need to find a way where fashion in general—both fast and slow—are operating within the planetary boundaries and have a positive impact instead of a negative one. You can play with the thought of super-fast fashion that you wear and put in the ground and it decomposes very quickly, enters back into the biological cycle very quickly, and it's made for one-time use."

A sustainable fast fashion requires a system where demand is also sustainable, and such a structure relies on changing both consumers' behaviors and some perceptual schemes of the fashion industry. Probably a new movement is needed to establish a sustainable trend, a movement that consists on spreading a new consumer trend, promoting 100% sustainable clothes, so first let's get a meaning of consumer trend because it is different from consumer behavior, as defined by the business dictionary "it is the habits or behaviors currently prevalent among consumers of goods or services. Consumer trends track more than simply what people buy and how much they spend. Data collected on trends may also include information such as how consumers use a product and how they communicate about a brand with their social network", so marketing a sustainable consumer trend can address the challenge of high demand and need for wearing long-lasting and compostable clothes, for example it could be emphasized through a sweet spot blending the need for sustainable brands, the use of innovations, and drivers of change.

To conclude, fast fashion appeared as a fast-consuming trend, so why not sharing a new mindset of purchasing a new kind of clothes, a process that affects the consumer psychology and engaging in a more conscious behavior, that will help to build a strong appeal for responsible purchasing power, in this way it will be possible to predict a fruitful future for sustainable fast fashion.

5 Conclusion

It appears that sustainability became the strategy used by the big fashion retailers, to some extent it could be perceived as a tactic to attract more customers and increase consumerism which falls in greenwashing activities, but it seems that it could also be the strategy for educating present and future generation toward a sustainable consumer trend that will address economic, social, and environmental sustainability at all the levels and at the same time, because these are complementary and constitute the mainstay of the well-functioning of a sustainable system. Furthermore, the spread of information is forcing large corporations to be more transparent for their actions.

With an ever-growing planetary challenge, the consumer cannot be anymore dumped even when they fall into greenwashing activities, there will always be a way to educate them, especially with the extensive work of some associations that keep watching and tracking even the smallest clothing manufacturer.

So, the future of sustainable fast fashion depends on the use of advanced technologies and innovations to be able to market a new consumer trend to foster the desire of quickly acquiring catwalk designs that follow both sustainable marketing strategy and manufacturing process.

References

Amy, W. (2015). *Two years after Rana Plaza, have conditions improved in Bangladesh's factories?* https://www.theguardian.com/sustainable-business/2015/apr/24/bangladesh-factories-building-collapse-garment-dhaka-rana-plaza-brands-hm-gap-workers-construction.

Buzzback.com. Buzzback+ Rainforest alliance Global study on sustainable.

Elkington, J. (1999). *Cannibals with forks: The triple bottom line of 21st century business.* https://link.springer.com/article/10.1023%2FA%3A1006129603978.

Fast Company. (2018). *Five innovations that could help make fast fashion more sustainable.* https://www.fastcompany.com/40537335/5-innovations-that-could-help-make-fast-fashion-more-sustainable.

Green Strategy. (2014). *A circular approach for the fashion industry.* http://www.greenstrategy.se/a-circular-approach-for-the-fashion-industry-2/.

Guinebeault, M. (2017). European textile/apparel imports and exports stable in 2016. http://hk.fashionnetwork.com/news/European-textile-apparel-imports-and-exports-stable-in-2016,802104.html#.WtbTKi5ubIU.

Hannah, G. (2017). *Zara and H&M back in-store recycling to tackle throwaway culture.* https://www.theguardian.com/sustainable-business/2017/may/26/zara-hm-step-up-instore-recycling-tackle-throwaway-culture.

https://www.ethicalfashionforum.com/the-issues/fast-fashion-cheap-fashion.

https://www.huffingtonpost.com/shannon-whitehead/5-truths-the-fast-fashion_b_5690575.html.

http://www.independent.co.uk/life-style/fashion/environment-costs-fast-fashion-pollution-waste-sustainability-a8139386.html.

https://www.investopedia.com/terms/f/fast-fashion.asp.

https://www.npr.org/2016/04/08/473513620/what-happens-when-fashion-becomes-fast-disposable-and-cheap.

https://www.npr.org/series/174306932/the-fast-world-of-fast-fashion.

Jana, K. (2016). *Rana Plaza collapse: Work place dangers persist three years later, reports find.* https://www.theguardian.com/business/2016/may/31/rana-plaza-bangladesh-collapse-fashion-working-conditions.

Marc, B. (2016). *Is H&M misleading customers with its talk of sustainability?* https://qz.com/662031/is-hm-misleading-customers-with-all-its-talk-of-sustainability/.

Mark, S. (2017). *It may not be possible to slow down fast fashion—so can the industry ever be sustainable?* https://www.independent.co.uk/life-style/fashion/it-may-not-be-possible-to-slow-down-fast-fashion-so-can-the-industry-ever-be-sustainable-a7970031.html.

Max-Neef, M., Elizalde, A., & Hopenhayn, M. (1991). *Human scale development: An option for the future.* Muscat: The Apex Press.

Rapport Brundtland

Social Responsibility case study: Patagonia and Esprit. https://www.njvid.net/show.php?pid=njcore:27960.

Sustainability reporting, H&M Group. http://sustainability.hm.com/en/sustainability/about/about/ceo-message.html.

Fashion Brands and Consumers Approach Towards Sustainable Fashion

Asimananda Khandual and Swikruti Pradhan

> *"You cannot get through a single day without having an impact on the world around you. What you do makes a difference, and you have to decide what kind of difference you want to make."*
>
> —Jane Goodall

Abstract 'Sustainable fashion' is one of the most widely used terms in the fashion industry today. It is not only about the trend of socially responsible brands with eco-friendly products or coming up with some regulatory policies but also for catering to upcoming demands of conscious consumers to adopt sustainable fashion. Consumers have evolved over the ages and have become educated about the materials and manufacturing process, which results in their growing interest to make socially responsible choices while updating their wardrobes with a value tag. In fact, International brands like Patagonia, People Tree, H&M, Thought, Indigenous, Rent the Runway, Stella McCartney have become more focused to approach fashion in as ethical and transparent manner as possible considering both environment and customers. Emerging slow fashion brands like 11.11, [Ka] [Sha], Doodlage, Raw Mango, Bodice, Rustic Hue etc. are dedicated to design and offer clothing made using fair and ethical means such as providing safe working conditions to the factory workers, working with handloom weavers and artisans to create handcrafted products, sourcing organic or recycled raw materials and up-cycling post-production and post-consumer wastes. The gradual shift from fast fashion to a sustainable and socially responsible fashion is clearly visible around the globe. Both new and old fashion brands, are undergoing transformation day by day with new business models, new age fashion labels and supply chain practices to address the awareness and demand for sustainable clothing. This chapter discusses on the forms of sustainable fashion, sustainable fashion

A. Khandual (✉)
Textile Engineering, College of Engineering & Technology (CET), Bhubaneswar, Odisha, India
e-mail: asimte@cet.edu.in

S. Pradhan
Rustic Hue, Bhubaneswar, Odisha, India
e-mail: swikruti.pradhan@gmail.com

© Springer Nature Singapore Pte Ltd. 2019   37
S. S. Muthu (ed.), *Fast Fashion, Fashion Brands and Sustainable Consumption*,
Textile Science and Clothing Technology,
https://doi.org/10.1007/978-981-13-1268-7_3

brands strategies, consumer transparency and the driving forces and scopes; how fashion brands and consumers are advancing towards sustainable fashion.

Keywords Sustainable fashion · Eco-friendly · Up-cycling
Post-consumer wastes · Bio-degradable · Slow fashion · Circular economy

1 Introduction

Sustainable fashion, with synonyms such as eco-fashion or green fashion or ethical fashion or slow fashion, has become a trending topic today. Where 'Fashion sustainability' is trending as a buzzword to gain attention and credibility, fashion brands are re-thinking about their business models and switching to more sustainable production and operation approaches. Consumers with growing awareness of the movement are supporting the brands that are environmentally conscious and produce ethically. Consumers' positive mindset towards sustainable brands with environment concern, business plans and techniques is increasing. The fashion industry has witnessed remarkable changes in terms of sustainability over the past few years.

'Sustainability' in fashion has become the major focus for long-term growth and environmental impact. Being the second most ecologically harmful industry with 1.5 million tons of waste, the fashion industry puts into landfills every year (Mahajan 2012). Sustainable fashion is becoming an expectation, as brands, designers, retailers, and manufacturers are becoming cognizant of the devastating effect of fast fashion on the surroundings (Grazia 2018). The chapter discusses how brands are making a wide variety of approaches to address this issue while consumers are shifting their focus to ethical shopping and conscious choices (Cataldi et al. 2010).

Fashion movements like #WhoMadeMyClothes are trying to bring transparency to the back end process of manufacturing to the consumers by keeping them informed (Fashion Revolution 2018). Consumers today want to pick styles meticulously not only to feel good about themselves but also how much they contribute to the person's life who makes them (Grazia 2018). Sustainability is now crucial for fashion businesses due to consumers' escalating consciousness about the ecosystem (Shen 2014).

This chapter explores various dimensions of sustainable fashion, sustainable fashion brands strategies, marketing transparency and the other driving forces, current and future trends; how fashion brands and consumers are advancing towards sustainable fashion.

2 Forms of Sustainable Fashion

Below are the forms of sustainable fashion from producer and consumer perspective (Fig. 1):

Custom made/Made-to-order

The garment should first be manufactured on demand or custom-made, in high quality and timeless design in an environment friendly manner. This form of sustainable fashion extends to the concept of DIY (Do-it-yourself).

Sustainable Design techniques/Production methods

Design can largely affect sustainability in fashion (Fig. 2).

Recycling means to reuse, while upcycling refers to the process of turning rejected articles into a product of greater value.

Upcycling involves the process of converting thrown away objects into a product of higher functionality by reducing waste, while recycling is often a chemical reconstruction of the materials to create a whole new product (Green Empowerment 2016).

Reconstruction is a form of Upcycling that involves deconstruction of previously worn garments or performed finished clothing products and then reconstruction into new designs. Zero-waste design techniques such as zero-waste pattern cutting, draping, smocking and plaiting eliminate waste at the design stage.

Indian design labels, Péro by Aneeth Arora and [Ka] [Sha] by Karishma Sahani Khan have strongly used Upcycling as a method in their collections. Studio Metallurgy, an Indian jewellery brand run by Advaeita Mathur had handcrafted jewellery

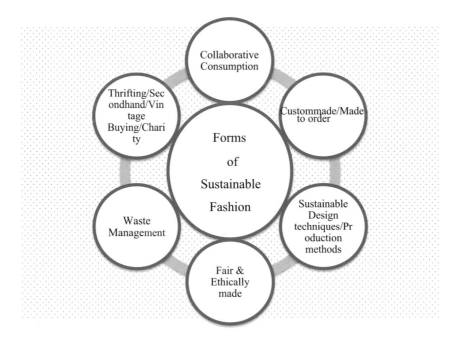

Fig. 1 Forms of sustainable fashion

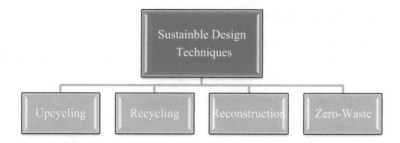

Fig. 2 Sustainable design techniques

out of plumbing washers while Amit Aggarwal of eponymous label AM.IT has constructed garments from discarded bindi sheets, recycled plastics and industrial materials (Better India 2016) (Fig. 3).

Apart from working with design techniques or adapting production methods considering the ethical impact, sourcing of raw materials is also an important factor. Natural fabrics must also be selected with prudence.

Yang Qin (2014) project that the global fibre production expected to reach 130 MT by 2025 and so as its growing waste in terms of textile, environment. Cotton as on today also grown with pesticides and require huge water inputs. Many unconventional

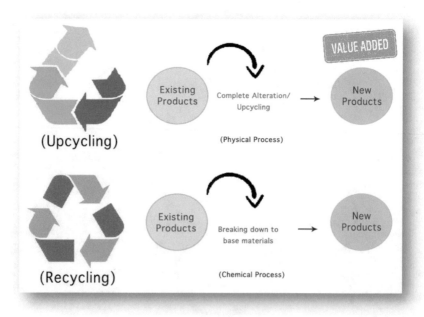

Fig. 3 Upcycling versus recycling

fibres (Khandual and Sahu 2016), such as bamboo seemingly a major candidate as a sustainable potential alternative. Specifically synthetic fibres such as polyester, nylon, and acrylic are well associated with the ecological dangers and biodegradability; those needed to be reduced/recycled or avoided. The use of organic cotton and fabrics is rising as one of the strongest resources to counter the adverse effects of regular cotton and cheaper synthetic alternatives. While the tag of 100% cotton is giving assurance to some, cotton farming still involves the use of pesticides. After the factory processing, the ready-to-use products in the store do not score much higher on the sustainability meter than synthetics. 11.11 and No Nasties are examples of brands using organic raw materials.

International design label Stella McCartney has been exploring ethical fashion since its set up in 2001. With her last collection in Paris Fashion Week, McCartney she hopes to get more support from people in this initiative and states that it's unavoidable that it will be part of the curriculum for consumption because the next generation needs a planet to live on and they deserve no less (The Guardian 2018). The use of unsustainable production methods may bring short-term gains in the competitive world but it would definitely boomerang in unexpected.

Fair & ethically made

The thumb rule in sustainable fashion is a product that supports the makers and their crafts. This form of sustainable fashion indicates production and procurement of raw materials, as well as the manufacturing, is done in such a way that pays fair wages to the workers or people living on the land, provides safe working condition respecting the environment and promotes sustainable farming (Grazia 2018).

Urban Austral is a brand working with local people in Patagonia to provide fair jobs and offers 100% handmade products made up of up-cycled materials. It donates 1% to REFORESTEMOS PATAGONIA, a tree plantation organization in the area.

Waste Management

Many consumers are unaware of the fact that a large chunk of their wardrobe is essentially plastic. More than 60% of the fibres are polyester that can look like silk, cotton, or soft faux fur, or which can be combined with natural materials to improve their performance and lower their cost. But consumers *are* very aware that the ocean is filling up with plastic. European brand C&A aims to replace virgin polyester made from petroleum with polyester made from certified recycled sources.

Bombshell Bay, a brand from Melbourne incorporates polyester made from recycled ocean plastics in their swimwear line, while Byron uses Econyl yarn spun from pre- and post-consumer nylon waste in the salt gypsy surf-wear. (https://bombshell bayswimwear.com, www.econyl.com).

New Delhi based ethical fashion manufacturer Conserve India pays waste pickers for all varieties of plastic waste and has so far transformed 12,000 tons of waste into belts and wallets that is sold in fair trade boutiques all over the world. It up-cycles waste like tire tubes, seat belts, fire hoses, cement bags, rice bags, packaging material. Waste-pickers supply 80% of the company's raw recyclable material. It has a design

Fig. 4 Scarps at Rustic Hue's studio

lab for experimenting with shapes and structures of new products since each material has to undergo different types of processing (Forbes 2017).

With great basics and an even greater concept, Aeon Row only uses recycled yarn to create their line. They work with revived fabrics and do not require land, water, chemicals, or cotton dyes to produce. Using fewer resources also means spending less money so it ends up being pocket friendly for consumers. The label puts effort to reduce environmental impact by keeping apparel out of landfills using revived fabrics in their designs and recycling old clothes (www.aeonrow.com).

Waste remains one of the biggest worries for sustainable design practitioners, as the clothing industry looks for ways to utilize the million tons of fabric are thrown away every year. Couture out of waste may sound like a hyperbole, but there are huge possibilities of reutilizing leftover and rejected fabrics to establish brands.

Kriti Tula, the designer of Delhi based emerging label Doodlage, is known as 'The Upcycler' (Vogue India, May 2018). She uses scraps of fabrics, industrial waste with organic cotton and sustainable materials. The label's AW16 collection was developed using corn and banana fabric to substitute cotton and yarn made entirely from spinning rejects. The collection 'Cloudwalker' was developed using techniques like patchwork, up-cycling small pieces of fabric and threads, which would otherwise have been rejected (www.doodlage.in).

Bhubaneswar based emerging label Rustic Hue works with local handloom weavers in the state to revive old textiles as well as enhancing product diversification and development through innovation. Secondly, the label upcycles post-production fabrics in its studio to create unique accessories. The accessories made up of fabric scraps are a part of their 'Jugaad' line (The Wall Art Magazine 2017) (Figs. 4 and 5).

Achieving a zero-waste level of production remains a difficult task, but most brands have started taking initiative by using various ways to minimize waste. The use of leftover fabrics to create trims like buttons, tassels, and embellishments, or crafting them has become common practice for designers.

Thrifting/Secondhand/Vintage Buying/Charity

Thrift and secondhand buying are currently en vogue. Customers are now becoming conscious about their buying decisions. They are mindfully spending their money while acknowledging that clothes need not necessarily drop their qualities just because they were pre-worn. Thrift stores not only offer pre-loved clothes at cheaper rates but also opportunity to develop one's sense of style.

NGOs and charities are essentially becoming the dumping ground with huge amount of lousy fast fashion products that can never be on-sold; this is another reason to support secondhand stores while rewinding our inclination towards fast fashion.

Collaborative Consumption

Over-consumption and a throwaway culture of products contribute to increased textile waste, which is becoming an environmental concern. Collaborative consumption is a concept that encourages the reuse of goods and reduces new shopping to prevent excessive textile waste. It's a socio-economic model different from traditional consumption that involves swapping, renting or trading instead of buying new products. The consumers not only contribute to minimizing textile waste but also benefit from sharing the production costs and reducing the burden of ownership (Lang and Armstrong 2018).

Fig. 5 Upcycled Chokers from fabric scraps

3   Sustainable Fashion Cycle

The concept of fashion product lifecycle suggests that every fashion product under-goes a cycle through different stages such as introduction, growth, maturity, and decline having a definite time period and the cycle is a bell-shaped curve. But sustainable clothing or textiles are considered to be classics or timeless for example, handloom weaves. Sustainable fashion products have high longevity and they neither 'go out of fashion' nor will rarely be 'in fashion'.

With various forms of sustainable fashion and conscious clothing decisions of the consumers, sustainable products last for long moving in a loop or circular manner where materials are recovered over and over again reducing waste. (Fashion Revolution 2018) (Fig. 6).

4   Gradual shift from fast fashion to slow fashion

"Fashion for everyone" is the motto of the fashion industry. Global citizens especially citizens in developed countries know they cannot keep consuming like we do now. The choices that the consumers are now left with are either to buy we ecological products to reduce the ecological footprint, or to reuse what they have now. This is the primary why consumers are making conscious clothing decisions and gradually heading towards sustainable fashion (Times Life 2018).

Fig. 6   A post shared by Fashion Revolution (@fash_rev) on Instagram

Sustainable fashion is a significant part of the transformation in the fashion industry across the globe. The three relationships between, Consumer-Environment, Brand-Environment and Consumer and Brand are highly influencing consumer receptivity and decision making for sustainable fashion brands.

The consumers are finding ways to embrace sustainable fashion in the real world. They realize that it is not as expensive as people think and they can explore various options for doing their bit (Grazia India 2018).

5 Sustainable Fashion Brands Strategies

Environmental sustainability is now being considered as a management agenda. It is being put on high priority across many fashion brands. It's all about maximizing benefits while minimizing negative impact. These brands are diving their society, environment, employees and customers in the right direction. Establishing a brand takes a much longer time than to spoil it. Design labels are adapting fair-trade practices, conscious design techniques like recycling and upcycling, and collaborating with craftspeople to bring in a sense of responsibility in their design creations.

Below are few strategies followed by eco fashion brands in current scenario:

1. *Digital Marketing (Digital Influencer Campaign)*

Brands realize that they need to connect with their customers in order to establish a strong relationship with them. They are putting strenuous effort to expand the emotional connection customers have with them by generating a more personal connection with marketing strategies like supporting charitable organizations, which are meaningful to their customers or offer ecologically friendly fashion choices. The digital influencer campaign is one such marketing strategy.

WORLD boots is focusing on creating brand awareness through an influencer campaign, that tunes well with the younger and more digitally savvy mass, and by presenting customers with top celebrities on social media platforms, sporting the trendy kicks. According to the brand designer, their customers want to be a part of the world around them even though they are present virtually online. They want the products with a completely new look but are also interested in knowing about the activities of the brand and supporting brands that become a part of a larger community, supporting worthwhile organizations like 'Soles for Souls'. They want to feel great about being part of something noble and the willingness will always be a part of the brand's business model (Kowalski 2017).

Acquiring visibility is a big challenge for emerging brands entering the market, especially when they face cutthroat competition with rich pockets and insider networks. But at the same time, these brands are free from burdens of preconceived notions of marketing and branding. They are fearlessly choosing to broaden their horizons by launching new, offbeat, socially conscious, and eco-friendly online campaigns.

2. *Alternative Marketing Strategy*

Alternative marketing plans work on the idea of using alternative media that includes both visual and textual content in order to make them more authentic and credible to communicate to the consumers and convey messages (Vuruskan and Frohlich 2012).

The "Be Stupid" campaign by Diesel was unconventional where the brand did not try to influence the consumers for ethical or sustainable way of thinking but definitely implied that every individual has freedom to make 'rebellious' choices and respect others' choices even if those are strange. The campaign encouraged consumers and included various forms of marketing communication - online, press and outdoor advertisements, a digital recruitment campaign for the Diesel music video and catalogue 2010, and viral activity streaming its philosophy and encouraged consumers to take risks moving beyond the smart and sensible way of life. The campaign invited acts and addressed an aspect of vanity and the promise to fulfill the need of social recognition and "fame" (Diesel 2012).

3. *Giving Back to the Society*

There are ethical brands that donate partial profits to a cause or community as part of their responsibility to give back to the society. With each purchase by a customer, a percentage goes into a mission they deeply care for. Hence the customer not only supports a sustainable product but also supporting a mission beyond the fashion industry.

New York City based fashion brand, SiiZU uses natural fabrics to create minimal designs that can be worn time and time again. With sustainability, proper fitting and sophistication as its core values, it donates 10% of each purchase to plant trees.

Berlin based ethical brand Abury collaborates with designers and artisans from craft clusters across the world to create exclusive handmade accessories collections with local materials and sells internationally. The Abury foundation pays fair wages to the community workers as well as invests in their education. Abury has given 125,982 h of education to the communities till now (www.abury.net) (Fig. 7).

4. *Showing transparency and keeping the consumers informed*

Svala, lets people learn more about the materials and business practices they use. It uses ethically sourced and produced natural and recycled materials.

a. **Carbon Offset Program**

Svala participates in a carbon-offset program to help reduce our carbon footprint from running the business, by calculating their monthly carbon footprint from the shipping and then buy carbon offsets to counteract this. The carbon offsets help fund projects such as planting trees and generating alternative energy from wind, solar and water.

b. **Local manufacturing and Sustainable packaging**

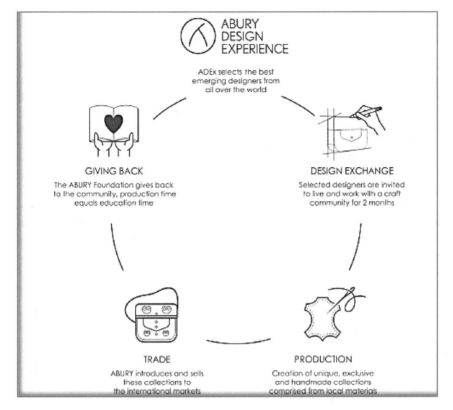

Fig. 7 Abury business model

The factory set up in LA ensures that the labourers are paid fairly and have comfortable working conditions. The brand labels and handbag dust bags are made up of organic cotton. The packaging materials and hangtags are made with a mixture of recycled kraft and hemp paper. (www.svala.co).

5. *Collaboration with Artisans*

Pagabags, an ethical brand works with artisans in West Africa supporting sustainable livelihoods. It creates unique bags using a woven blend of vibrantly colored local cotton threads and recycled plastic bags. It also uses traditional batiks, mud-painted cotton, faso dan fani cloth ("woven cloth of the homeland") wax and non-toxic dyes.

After witnessing their traditions & creativity in weaving and sewing, Meredyth Bowler Ailloud, the founder, knew there was so much potential and she wanted to share it with the world. They have partnered with a handful of men and 40 women waste collectors, plastic cutters, weavers, sewers, batik makers and bead-makers. They also provide healthcare and on-site professional training. The brand not only thinks about the impact they have on the planet but also enrich the lives of others who need it most.

6. *Product diversification and value addition—Innovation on the loom (Example: Raw Mango)*

Raw Mango, an Indian brand is about celebrating Indian traditional weaves along with upliftment of an entire community by spawning a new value for an existing and misheeded product. Handloom Saris* though worn by a huge mass in India, remains a domain perceived to have hardly any scope for new explorations, Raw Mango's authentic and respectful design interventions in different craft clusters in India such as Chanderi, Mushru silk of Gujarat, Benarasi have been able to make the product simple, sophisticated, contemporary and fresh with strikingly bright colour palette. The designs rooted to Indian philosophies and traditions are a reflection of more than 450 skilled craftsmen it works with (www.rawmango.in).

The brand debuted in Lakmé India Fashion Week Winter/Festive 2014 with its ready-to-wear collection in clean and simple silhouettes in empire line midi, maxi, paneled gown, saris, lehenga, lean kurta, quilted jackets and sherwanis in jewel tones of electric pink, dark blue, peach, gold white and parrot green with beautiful golden motifs of birds, flowers and intricate traditional designs. The entire collection was developed by artisans in Benaras using Kadwa Brocade technique, which is ornamentation with extra weft on the loom (Verve Magazine 2014).

*The traditional outer garment of women in the Indian subcontinent, worn with one end wrapped around the waist to form a skirt with pleats, the other draped over the shoulder or head (Concise Oxford English Dictionary, 2018)

7. *Thoughtful Design Philosophy (Example: Bodice)*

Indian fashion designer Ruchika Sachdeva founded her eco-fashion label 'Bodice' in 2011 that has won many awards such as International Wool Mark Prize 2017/18, Vogue India Fashion Fund 2014, Elle Design award to name a few. The label makes conscious choices about materials used for clothing that would not be responsible for damaging the environment in any way. It not only offers beautiful clothes but also includes elements like a change in size so that they can last for a longer time and can be worn in many occasions, for example, some of the designs can be increased or reduced by 4". The designs of the label are eco-friendly, sustainable and thoughtful.

6   Consumer Awareness and Approach

"A fresh generation is marching for revolution and they want to wear clothes that tell a new story. Let's give it to them."—Naomi Klein (Author, Social Activist & Film Maker)

Clothing is the basic need for human beings, but in the middle of a fast fashion culture, the industry has ended up witnessing serious consecutions for people and the planet (McNeill and Moore 2015). Eco-fashion has become a key trend for consumers especially the young mass (Niinimäki 2010).

Documentaries, public campaigns, celebrities, and political figures have all made ethical fashion a major buzzword. Recently, in an interview, His Royal Highness—The Prince of Wales, Prince Charles shared his views on sustainable fashion and how the challenges can be tackled in the industry. He believes in the concept of reuse, repair or mending clothes instead of just throwing them away. He feels the need of growing awareness among consumers to head towards a circular type of economy (Australian Financial Review 2018) (Fig. 8).

Emma Watson (Actor, Activist, UN Goodwill Ambassador, Time's Up Advocate) made a media buzz with her five-piece red carpet look in monochrome at the Met Gala 2016 designed by Calvin Klein. The body part of the outfit was formed from three different kinds of fabrics all woven from yarns out of recycled plastic bottles, the zippers from recycled materials and the inner bustier from organic cotton. Not only the materials, the entire outfit was also repurposed and could be used as separates with different styling in future (The Telegraph UK, May 2016). Emma has been a strong supporter of eco-fashion, which is clearly evident when she wore outfits approved by sustainability consulting group Eco Age for the promotion of her films 'Beauty and the Beast' and 'The Circle' and documented it on Instagram (The Cut 2018). As a guest editor of March 2018 issue of Vogue Australia which themed 'Designing the Future', she shares her view on sustainable fashion, encourages everybody to be

fash_rev • Follow

fash_rev Prince Charles calls for sustainable fashion in today's @financialreview @afrmag 🌱

His Royal Highness the Prince of Wales ('HRH') chatted to staunch fashion revolutionary and international fashion editor @marion.hume about the critical environmental challenges faced by the global fashion industry.
"It is extraordinary how fashions change and, speaking as someone who, on the whole, hates throwing away things without finding another use for them or mending them, I couldn't be more delighted if, at last, there is a growing awareness of the urgent need to get away from the 'throwaway society' and to move towards a more 'circular economy."
#PREACH 🙌
He also speaks about his personal approach to fashion, saying: "I have always believed in

♡ ◯   🔖

5,517 likes

4 DAYS AGO

Add a comment...   •••

I have always believed in trying to keep as many of my clothes and shoes going for as long as possible... through patches and repairs — and in this way I tend to be in fashion once every 25 years...

— PRINCE CHARLES —

Fig. 8 A post shared by Fashion Revolution (@fash_rev) on Instagram

thoughtful about fashion and challenges to all make a one-degree shift as a small change to bring in a huge difference (Vogue Australia 2018) (Fig. 9).

Furthermore, caring about the movement on eco fashion, she shows her concern for the makers, workers, and manufacturers in the fashion industry (Fig. 10).

Ethical fashion consultancies, e-commerce sites, and fashion bloggers are becoming more popular and influencing the consumers massively. While emergent design labels are spinning new yarns in design, the consumers are becoming more socially conscious showing concerns for the environment (Gwilt and Rissanen 2012).

With the constant technological advancements and increase in popularity of social media platforms such as Facebook, Instagram, Twitter and Snapchat, consumers are being highly influenced to engage and participate in fashion in a more meaningful manner.

As this trend grows, customers don't mind paying a bit extra to invest in green clothes—and a green fashion future (Shen et al. 2012). If consumers develop making choices to buy an outfit made up of a recycled material or anew fibre, such as cruelty-free leather made in a lab, then they will are support start-up companies creating new markets, and avoiding the negative impacts associated with conventional textiles.

According to Erin Lewis-Fitzerland who works on a project named Visible Mending in Melbourne, most clothing problems can easily be repaired, for example missing buttons, loose stitching etc. Mending gives an opportunity to craft the clothes better than the new. One creatively mended garment can inspire two other people to start mending and become more aware even if it alone cannot save the planet. Mending

Fig. 9 Outfits using recycled plastic yarns and organic cotton at the Met Gala 2016

it's not enough for me anymore that it's a beautiful item. I want to know who made it and where it came from

– EMMA WATSON –

fash_rev • Follow

fash_rev Emma Watson wants to know #whomademyclothes... "It's not enough for me anymore that it's a beautiful piece — I want to know who made it and where it came from". Read more in this month's edition of @vogueaustralia, guest edited by @emmawatson, dedicated to conversations about sustainability and 'Designing the Future'. #fashionrevolution

Load more comments

velvetdreams

mia.strada.london AMEN

marsisnotjustaplanet
@marsisnotjustaplanet

iamrobert_black @marize.malan

nomadsclothing We love this!

beautybykahliya

alisa.moltkehuitfeldt @annamoltkehuitfeldt

7,370 likes

MARCH 14

Add a comment...

Fig. 10 Post shared by Fashion Revolution (@fash_rev) on Instagram, 2018

can expand the lifespan of wardrobe. Once clothing becomes tired and hole-ridden, it can be mended instead of being thrown to garbage.

The impact of fashion clothing and textiles on climate change has given us all to rethink our choices and buying decisions (Grazia 2018). Consumers are encouraged to pay attention to the story behind the outfit they want, the maker and its area of production, check certification and usage labels, research the brands instead of falling for dubious claims. Even though the attractions of fast fashion are undeniably strong, but one thing is quite transparent that slow and sustainable wins the race (Sustainably Chic 2017).

7 Scope

Sustainability is not free from challenges. There are many standards to achieve from ensuring minimal carbon footprint to utilization of leftover fabrics. The use of organic raw materials, fair trade practices and artful management also makes clothing more expensive compared to the mass-produced products. But in the long run, sustainable fashion breaks even by lasting longer—and getting better with wash and wear with a positive impact on artisans as well. The awareness about sustainable fashion is in a nascent stage as it is still not as popular as fast fashion. The main drawback in going eco is the cost factor. The use of sustainable fashion products and materials will cost much more than using conventional materials in some cases. The manufacturers fear that the increase in cost will make clothes pricier and beyond the reach of ordinary families with middle-class economic background.

The textile manufacturers need to spend more time on research and development of methods and materials in order to transform into an eco brand. So, time is an important factor, which may be a disadvantage for them. They also need to focus on sourcing of eco-friendly materials and appointing trained people who would be able to use them.

Muthu et al. (2012a, b), Dahlbo et al. (2017) extensively studies about the carbon foot prints in Increased textile circulation their consequences and remedial majors for *Sustainable Production and Consumption*. These are clear ecological indicators and needed to be addressed very carefully well before they create major detrimental issues in near future. Solvent free processing, use of organic textile auxiliaries, natural dye, use of novel technologies like ultrasonic assisted processing, plasma and nanotechnology has been expanding new direction in eco-friendly wet processing. Jena et al. (2015), Khandual et al. (2015, 2016), Barik et al. (2017) discussed some fundamental ideas of ecological processing and alternative finish directives for textiles.

The fear of price points and the acceptability by customers are not always the key factor. Moreover, the sustainable fashion may widen the range of consumers' options. Sustainable fashion is likely to lead and rule fashion diversity, beyond being driven by fashion trends and seasons when brands' innovation blend with local resources.

8   Conclusion

From the current point of view of designing clothes, much attention are now being paid whether, those are sustainably produced and are fashionable—they have to be something that people want to wear with a socially responsibility. Fashion is a language through which one's individuality is expressed. Customers want to feel great about their clothes, and that includes feeling great about how they were made with a concern of social responsibility. Fair wages and happy workers are being included in ethical policies—and they are a strong selling point too.

Switching to fashion that is more ethical option does take forethought; the health of the planet and the safety of workers in developing nations are taken seriously. Ethical fashion must be promoted for a secure, healthy and sustainable future.

It is the collective responsibility of everyone in the product value chain from producer to final consumer, to ensure that no harm to the surroundings during the overall cycle of production and consumption. It is essential to value our environment and traditional craft heritage for true growth and prosperity as unsustainable practices can give immediate benefits but it will strike back in the long run.

References

10 Hot Stories, no-7. (2018). Is high street sustainability an oxymoron, *Grazia, TOI, 10*(12), 54–54.

Barik, S., Khandual, A., Behera, L., Badamali, S. K., & Luximon, A. (2017). Nano-Mg–Al-layered double hydroxide application to cotton for enhancing mechanical, UV protection and flame retardancy at low cytotoxicity level. *Cellulose, 24*(2), 1107–1120.

Cataldi, C., Dickson, M., & Grover, C. (2010). Slow fashion: Tailoring a strategic approach towards sustainability.

Dahlbo, H., Aalto, K., Eskelinen, H., & Salmenperä, H. (2017). Increasing textile circulation—Consequences and requirements. *Sustainable Production and Consumption, 9,* 44–57.

Feel-Good Fashion. (2018, April 1). Times Life, TOI, Nupur Amarnath, 1–4.

Gwilt, A., & Rissanen, T. (2012). *Shaping sustainable fashion: Changing the way we make and use clothes*. Abingdon: Routledge.

https://www.instagram.com/p/BeVEgCcg_CS/?taken-by=fash_rev. Accessed on June 7, 2018

https://www.instagram.com/p/BhOavV4A2VP/?taken-by=fash_rev. Accessed on June 7, 2018

https://www.instagram.com/p/BE7UT8gH3GF/?taken-by=emmawatson. Accessed on June 8, 2018

https://www.instagram.com/p/BgStFnuAgyX/?taken-by=fash_rev. Accessed on June 8, 2018

http://www.rawmango.in/collections/. Accessed on 10 April 2018.

https://svala.co/pages/about-us. Accessed on 10 April 2018.

https://abury.net/. Accessed on 14 April 2018.

https://www.doodlage.in/ourstory/. Accessed on 7 April 2018.

https://www.aeonrow.com/. Accessed on 9 April 2018.

http://thewallartmag.com/design-supplement. (Jyotsna Sharma, July 26, 2017). Accessed on 14 April 2018.

http://www.afr.com/afr-special/prince-charles-how-fashion-can-be-sustainable-20180201-h0rv11 Marion Hume, April 6, 2018. Accessed on 6 April 2018.

https://www.forbes.com/sites/ashoka/2017/10/16/waste-collection-a-new-frontier-for-the-fashion-industry/#42d082b77149. Ashoka, October 16, 2017, 09:49 AM. Accessed on 9 April 2018.

https://www.telegraph.co.uk/fashion/events/met-gala-2016-emma-watson-wears-a-calvin-klein-dress-made-from-r/ (Emma Spedding, May 3, 2016 10:45am). Accessed on 14 April 2018.

https://www.thecut.com/2018/02/emma-Watson-guest-edits-vogue-australias-march-issue.html. Sarah spellings (The Cut; February 19, 2018). Accessed on 13 April 2018.

https://www.theguardian.com/fashion/2018/mar/05/ethical-fashion-stella-mccartney-paris-fashion-week Hannah Marriott, 5 March 2018 14.43 GMT. Accessed on 9 April 2018.

https://www.vogue.com.au/fashion/news/emma-watson-introduces-the-march-2018-issue-of-vogue-australia/image-gallery/5531be4141980e0597ead6372d08f09a?pos=1. (Vogue Australia, March 2018). Accessed on 13 April 2018.

https://www.thebetterindia.com/88846/india-sustainable-fashion/. Sohini Dey, February 24, 2017, 6.45 PM. Accessed on 10 April 2018.

http://www.vervemagazine.in/fashion-and-beauty/lakme-fashion-week-day-2.

Jena, B., Das, B. P., Khandual, A., Sahu, S., & Behera, L. (2015). Ecofriendly processing of textiles. *Materials Today: Proceedings, 2*(4–5), 1776–1791.

Khawani, M. P., & Khatwani, P. A. (2017) Indian textiles: Its sustainability and global sourcing. *International Journal of Recent Innovation in Engineering and Research 2*(7), 26–29.

Khandual, A. (2016). Green flame retardants for textiles. In *Green fashion* (pp. 171–227). Singapore: Springer.

Khandual, A., & Sahu, S. (2016). Sabai grass: Possibility of becoming a potential textile. In *Sustainable fibres for fashion industry* (pp. 45–60). Singapore: Springer.

Khandual, A., Luximon, A., Sachdeva, A., Rout, N., & Sahoo, P. K. (2015). Enhancement of functional properties of cotton by conventional dyeing with TiO_2 nanoparticles. *Materials Today: Proceedings, 2*(4–5), 3674–3683.

Lang, C., & Armstrong, C. M. J. (2018). Collaborative consumption: The influence of fashion leadership, need for uniqueness, and materialism on female consumers' adoption of clothing renting and swapping. *Sustainable Production and Consumption, 13,* 37–47.

Mahajan, S. (2012). Sustainability of green fashion. In *International conference: Textiles and fashion 2012* (pp. 1–11).

McNeill, L., & Moore, R. (2015). Sustainable fashion consumption and the fast fashion conundrum: fashionable consumers and attitudes to sustainability in clothing choice. *International Journal of Consumer Studies, 39*(3), 212–222.

Muthu, S. S., Li, Y., Hu, J. Y., & Mok, P. Y. (2012a). Quantification of environmental impact and ecological sustainability for textile fibres. *Ecological Indicators, 13*(1), 66–74.

Muthu, S. S., Li, Y., Hu, J. Y., & Ze, L. (2012b). Carbon footprint reduction in the textile process chain: recycling of textile materials. *Fibers and Polymers, 13*(8), 1065–1070.

Niinimäki, K. (2010). Eco-clothing, consumer identity, and ideology. *Sustainable Development, 18*(3), 150–162.

Shen, B. (2014). Sustainable fashion supply chain: Lessons from H&M. *Sustainability, 6*(9), 6236–6249.

Shen, B., Wang, Y., Lo, C. K., & Shum, M. (2012). The impact of ethical fashion on consumer purchase behavior. *Journal of Fashion Marketing and Management: An International Journal, 16*(2), 234–245.

Vuruskan, A., & Frohlich, J (2012). Alternative marketing strategies in commercial eco fashion. pp.126–130. http://dergipark.gov.tr/download/article-file/275396.

Yang Qin, M. (2014). Global fibres overview. Synthetic Fibres Raw Materials Committee Meeting at APIC 2014. Pattaya, 16 May 2014. http://www.orbichem.com/userfiles/APIC%202014/APIC 2014_Yang_Qin.pdf.

Printed in the United States
By Bookmasters